Telling Tales Out Of School

Edited and typeset by Paul Crick at
Paul Crick Publishing and Editorial Consultancy, Norwich

Cover production by Rosie and Tony Clarke at
Spirit Studio, Perth, Australia

ISBN: 978-178456-783-5
Paperback

First published 2021 by Upfront Publishing
Peterborough, England.

An environmentally friendly book printed and bound in England
by www.printondemand-worldwide.com

Telling Tales Out Of School

Telling Tales
Out Of School

Chris Lowe

Illustrated by Chris Ellard and Steve Lancaster

Introduction

Taking the Register

It all began with Mary, my wife, insisting that I should get rid of the mountain of old diaries, notebooks and files from my study. I had been promising the clear-out for some years, but the Covid 19 lockdown in March 2020 was the clincher. It was to be my pandemic therapy. But before I had even opened the filing cabinet I had a counter-wheeze; I would turn the mass of yellowing bits of paper into stories, anecdotes and yarns. It would be my lockdown project, a Scheherazadan task of 'a tale a day', and I would send them to family and friends to read – or maybe delete. And so *Telling Tales out of School* was born.

The daily exercise began immediately after the lockdown in March and ended 101 days later on what was by happenchance my birthday in July. Since then, over thirty more have been penned at random intervals. Lots of friends chipped in with ideas, anecdotes, poems, cartoons and tales of their own.

The Tales, although you might find it difficult to believe this, are all founded on true events, or are stories told to me by real teachers with impeccable reputations for verisimilitude! They have, of course, been transmuted as I have recollected them in the tranquility of retirement. They are stories, anecdotes, yarns about growing up, learning and teaching together, coping together and form a chronicle of school life in the latter half of the twentieth century, when human relationships, behaviour and attitudes were being reshaped after the Second World War and the enormous changes to home-life and to society in general. Schools were not immune from the upheaval going on. Habits, behaviour, and even the law, were different then, but were changing. They shaped the new relationships that were being forged in the new 'comprehensive school' era.'

But teachers' and pupils' responses to what life throws at them are timeless. Behind them is my sense that teaching and learning are a branch of the entertainment business. In order to best inform and educate their learners, schools must entertain and enchant. Schools are fun – or at least funny.

The idea for this book, *Telling Tales Out of School*, came out of a discussion with my former colleague, Jenny Blount, who is a trustee of the James Rutterford Trust, a charity helping pupils who need financial support for school activities, etc at Prince William School, Oundle, the school in North Northamptonshire where I had been Head for twenty-eight years. I offered to donate the stories to the Trust. Jenny and the Chair of the Trust, Pat Rutterford, were enthusiastic and so were the other trustees, including Elizabeth Dormor, the present Headteacher. And so without further ado, we found ourselves a brilliant editor, brilliant illustrators, and a brilliant designer. Hence the book was born.

Fifty of the original Tales appear in this book, a difficult choice. Plenty more tales remain on file for future publication, if this first volume is greeted with favour.

I am no Chaucer, Shakespeare or Dickens but I share their goal: to depict the human comedy all around us and in my case in every nook and cranny of schools, colleges and universities. Schooldays for the vast majority of us remain 'the happiest days of our life' when one looks back at them. If the Tales raise in you just one smile or one nod of recognition, then I am content. Two smiles would be a bonus.

All proceeds from sales of the book will go to the James Rutterford Trust and other educational charities.

Chris Lowe
Cheswardine, 2021

About the Author

Chris Lowe CBE, TD, D Ed, MA, LL B was a headteacher of a secondary school in Northamptonshire for 28 years, after teaching in Croydon and Leicester.

Born and educated in Newcastle-under-Lyme, Staffordshire, he went on to Cambridge University after spending his National Service as an infantry officer in The North Staffordshire Regiment. He obtained degrees in English at Cambridge, and Law at the University of London.

In 1990–91 Chris was President of the Secondary Heads Association (now the Association of School and College Leaders) followed by four years as President of the European School Heads Association.

He was made a Commander of the British Empire (CBE) in 1992 and was awarded the Territorial Decoration (TD) in 1973. He has also received an honorary doctorate from De Montfort University, and been elected to Honorary Fellowships of both the University of Wolverhampton and University of Northampton. For three years Chris was a Visiting Professor of Education Law at the Edith Cowan University, Perth, Western

Australia, and for five years he was Chair of the Royal Opera House, Covent Garden Education Council and a member of the Board of the Royal Opera House.

Since retirement he has set up a company specialising in providing compliance support to schools and academies (www.handsam.education)

Chris lives in Shropshire with his wife, Mary.

The James Rutterford Trust

The James Rutterford Trust was established in 1993 by Pat and Ron Rutterford following the tragic and untimely death of their son James, at the age of 21. James was a former student of Prince William School, Oundle where he was a member of the school Army Cadets; his legacy still lives on with the James Rutterford Memorial Trophy for best recruit, which is awarded annually at the Presentation and Enrolment Ceremony.

He also enjoyed helping with the Duke of Edinburgh Award scheme weekends away.

James was passionate about offering local youngsters their own leisure activities. There was relatively little for young people to do in the late 1980s, and he was very committed to providing entertainment through his regular local discos, which continue to be very fondly remembered to this day.

It is a rare thing indeed for a young man, taken from us so early in his life, to continue to have such a positive influence on the local community.

Over the last 28 years, the Trust has provided financial support for students of the school, to enable them to take part in school activities, to provide equipment to aid their studies, and to support the full range of school opportunities and experiences, both academic and social. The Trust is a truly local charity, receiving donations from local people and local businesses.

The *Telling Tales Out of School* project is a marvellous opportunity for us to raise the profile of the charity as well as raising much-needed funds to continue the work we do. We are truly grateful to you, Chris, for this most generous gift of your book, which will ensure that we can continue to help and encourage local young people to access and enjoy the whole experience of school life and not only what goes on in the classroom.

For more information and to donate to the Trust please visit:
https://donatemyschool.com/jamesrutterfordtrust

MORNING ASSEMBLY

Funny Places

Schools are funny places – funny peculiar and funny ha ha.

Funny peculiar, because what sort of person in their right mind – if they had the choice – would put thirty adolescents in a room with one adult and then close the door? And then repeat the process for 1,000 hours each year – for at least twelve years, eh? Most parents are exhausted from looking after two children for the six-week summer school holidays. How would you feel if I told you that you had to carry on looking after your progeny for another thirty-four weeks?

That is also why schools are funny ha ha. Teachers and the taught have to survive and thrive, and so schools are inevitably part of the entertainment industry, aren't they? When you meet in pubs and clubs it is not the challenge of French irregular verbs, or how quadratic equations have helped you through life, or the value of the cosine formula to the wealth of nations that dominate the conversation. It is what Mr Whatsit did to the wastepaper basket one memorable Friday afternoon and what Miss Thingy said to Darren when he asked her if she had a boyfriend. It is the same the world over.

And it was pure indulgence in nostalgia that inspired Marcus Brampton and five old friends to meet up again, thirty years after their year's Postgraduate Certificate in Education course together.

They met in The Babbling Brook, the pub that they had frequented in their student days, close to the hall of residence. But gone was the tile floor, the long bar and the noise of a hundred thirsty students. Now one of the best eateries in the city of two universities and twenty-thousand students, it described itself as a 'gastro-pub': discreet lighting, printed menus, tablecloths ... and waiters. There wasn't a student in sight, except for the waiters, just a family of four in the far corner and a couple dining just behind the large round table at

3

which the new arrivals were seated. They certainly lifted the level of animation.

After the hugs and patting on the back and tucking into Thai curry, boeuf bourguignon and poulet à la provençale, they launched into the serious business of reminiscing. Marcus started the party going.

'It strikes me that this is a bit like Chaucer meeting his fellow pilgrims at The Tabard in Chiswick six hundred years ago. Didn't they meet 'at nyght in that hostelrye'?'

'They certainly did,' said primary school teacher Ruth, with her well-remembered forthright vigour, 'but I am not walking to Canterbury with you or anyone else, so here the comparison ends!'

She turned to their oldest friend, Clive.

'You're our Chaucer, Clive. You've got a degree in English and always told a good story. Tell us what you have been up to, or perhaps tell us about the lesson you remember best.'

Clive Dare, known throughout his life as 'Dan Dare' was indeed their daddy figure, a refugee from the world of City of London finance dealings, who felt he just wanted to do something to be remembered by. Teaching seemed a good idea.

'Well, as you know,' began Clive, 'I ended up as a Principal, but actually my most memorable lesson was the very first one I ever took, and it came in the year before I joined the certificate course. I wanted to find out if I could actually teach and so when I left the City, and all that frantic wheeling and dealing, I accepted a temporary post to teach English at a small independent boys' school out in the sticks, miles from anywhere.

'It was an 'exclusive' school, not in the sense that it was keen on excluding pupils – as one of my subsequent inner-city schools was – but 'exclusive' to any but the sons and occasional daughters of the wealthy – pop stars, city slickers, film stars, TV celebrities, industrial magnates and the like – those who were pro having children, but anti having them around the home. You've all met the sort.

'What the kids had in common was that they had indeed been excluded from their original schools for activity or non-activity that the school had disapproved of and finally despaired of. That's why it was exclusive and why there was a job for the totally unqualified like me.'

'I never knew you had been teaching before,' said Ruth. 'Must have been very useful.'

'Actually it was not a very auspicious start, but I learned more in the first forty-five minutes teaching at that school than I did on my whole year's teaching certificate course.'

This sounded like just the gripping start they needed! A bit of mystery, a trifle of titillation. Clive continued.

*****

Because I had not applied for the job until the middle of the summer school holidays, I didn't know which English groups I would be teaching until the staff meeting on the morning of the first day. At the time I thought this was normal, not simply a result of the school's uncanny disregard for administrative niceties, which it actually was!

I never met the Head. Never, until the day I left. Mr Cesare Insalata was a somewhat remote, begowned figure who glided round the building like the school ghost, always glimpsed just disappearing round a corner or up a staircase. His family owned the school. They saw an opportunity in this huge damp and decrepit Victorian pile deep in the West Country. The school had been founded in a Pembrokeshire farmhouse by his Neapolitan great-grandfather. He was a refugee shoemaker who, on his way to America, had paused to catch breath in Haverfordwest, seen a gap for an ice-cream business, and made a killing. Teaching the children of immigrants followed and now a string of independent schools are just a small part of the Insalata empire.

It was the Deputy Head who really managed all the school affairs except, that is, for the money. He appointed me, found accommodation for me nearby, and met me at the front door at eight o'clock on the opening day, greeting me with one hand and giving me my timetable with the other.

'Staff meeting at 8.30am Dare, while Mr Insalata takes school assembly and prayers. Classes begin at ten o'clock. I'll be available after morning school if you have any questions. I don't expect you will have. You haven't been here long enough.' And with that he was gone.

Once I had found my locker, which was at the back of the storeroom, and then found my Head of Department, who was at the back of another storeroom, stuffing what looked like a bottle of Teachers into his locker, I trundled along to the staff meeting, perusing my timetable on the way.

I noted that all my classes were denoted B or C and in one case R. Even though I would have liked an A group I thought I could cope with Bs and Cs. But an R Group? R?! This was disconcerting. The only R group I had ever come across was in the Billy Bunter books, where his nickname was the 'Fat Owl of the Remove'. I confess I had never understood what it signified.

'My new colleagues did not help much when I raised the matter in the staffroom after the formal staff meeting, taken, as I gather it always was, by the Deputy Head.

'The Remove, eh? So, they've given you one of those? Well I never, tut tut!' This was Joshua Pasternak, my Head of Department – allegedly – who had announced his intention to

retire at Christmas. Many of his colleagues thought he had retired years ago. But no, he was still there, in body if not spirit. And he thought it was entirely appropriate to end his days with a flourish of taking entirely A groups. Mr Pasternak knew very well that I was down to take the 5th Remove, and I knew he knew!

'Well, how can I best describe the Remove? Hmm?' Another voice cut in. Someone with authority and know-how, I mused.

'It's not difficult to describe them. They are the sort of boys whose parents don't mind paying fees and don't mind too much about what they are taught ...'

It was an elderly colleague from his armchair, in an academic gown which had once been black but was now a patchy olive green and grey, patinated by age and pipe smoke. I learned later that this was Bertram Catchpole, who had arrived at the school forty years previously after being invalided out of the Great War, and whose passion, and sole interest now, was running the school army cadets.

'... and who don't ask too many questions,' he added, waving his pipe airily in my direction, sending curls of blue smoke spiralling expertly up to the ceiling.

That wasn't what I was looking for, I must confess. I still had no idea what to expect of the boys – and no-one had mentioned the girls at all. I tried another tack.

'Do the pupils care? About their education, I mean?' I said, addressing the room generally.

There was a sort of shuffling and clearing of throats.

'Oh yes, some do, and some don't – sometimes...' Not encouraging responses.

Then another voice cut in.

'If you can show them how your subject helps them make money, you'll be fine. Business Studies and Economics are popular. They also like arithmetic but are not all that keen on quadratic equations and geometry, I have noted.' Archie Meades, Head of Science – and the only qualified science teacher – tapped his pipe out on an ashtray and leaned back contemplatively. He was trying to be positive, but his advice was not much help to someone teaching them English literature.

He, too, waved his pipe in my direction. 'Don't give the blighters an inch or they'll take a mile.' Once again Archie thought he was offering timeless sound advice to a young whippersnapper. But I felt my heart sink a little.

'You should try entertaining them – they like being amused.' This was the contribution of the school's only historian, Jonathan Swift, also from a sedentary position. 'Frobisher here has no trouble entertaining them, do you Frobe? They start laughing as soon as Frobe enters the room.

'Yes,' said Frobisher looking up from his marking, 'I do seem to have the ability to stimulate hilarity, even though there is not much fun in Virgil's *Aeneid* at their level, I must admit. They keep on demanding the racier – I would call them 'vulgar' – Catullus poems, the ones towards the back of the anthology. They do like the Lesbia poems, but I have given them up now since young Brace started writing his own and selling them.'

'You should admire their ability to turn anything into cash, Frobe. It's what pays our wages! And that's what they will be doing all their lives, isn't it? When it is announced that another one of the Remove has made his next billion in computers, steel, or potatoes, you can pat yourself on your back, Frobe, and say it was all down to Lesbia's thousand kisses.'

'It's not her kisses that worry me, Swift, no I don't mind the kisses, but—'

The bell went and Catullus's more salacious adventures would have to wait. All of that was something I had to digest for the future. Right now it wasn't the Fifth that I was kicking off my teaching career with for the first period on that first day. It was 4C. The phrase '4C English' has more brooding menace than 'Year 10 English Mr Dare's Group', I think, even though both are classes of twenty-odd fifteen-year-olds.

Most of 4C were destined for next year's 5th Remove, I was sure. But for the time being there was faith and hope. Charity would be a bonus. I fancied my chances. I was, after all, a

Territorial Army officer, I had fought my corner in the City, and I could still remember how the best of my own teachers had gone about their job.

'Off to feed the wolves you go, Harrison,' chuckled one colleague, waving his hand in the direction of the staffroom door. I smiled back at him, ignoring the fact that Mr Thingamajig had used my predecessor's name.

On my way to the classroom, I decided that making an impact was the right thing to do. It had worked well enough when I was a pupil, and it did now – initially at least. The class comprised sons (and a few daughters) of the great monied middle class and so fell dutifully silent and watchful when I burst in and, as purposefully as I could manage, strode to the teacher's desk.

They settled back and awaited events, as all classes do when a new teacher arrives. They were eager to test out this new victim. I could sense that immediately. But I felt well enough prepared, just as I had done on a hundred practice night attacks on Territorial Army exercises. But I also knew that even the best-laid plans do not survive the first encounter with the enemy, so I remained alert – or rather, wary.

I had already decided that to break the ice and gain some breathing space I needed to learn their names. I remembered that this is what teachers had always done. It seemed a good idea, the sort of thing you should do on your first day. So, having inscribed all their names in neat rows that I had drawn in my notebook, and after handing out a set of readers, I told them they were going to read around the class. I would, randomly, indicate who was going to read next and when – so they had better pay attention.

They did.

All went rather well for the first fifteen minutes. R M Ballantyne's *Coral Island* was as good a book as any for fifteen-year-olds – and in any case it was the only full set of readers left in the department store cupboard. Boy after boy and occasional girl read a paragraph with varying interpretations and mixture of unlikely accents, designed no doubt to test the new teacher's patience level and stickability. But I was not going to succumb to intimidation. Each reader's efforts were applauded by 'Sir'. I was in front by a short head, I reckoned. Then as I moved to the other half of the class, I noticed out of the corner of my eye one lad on my left, who was clearly in a world of his own, staring into space and not at the page.

'You, boy. Name?' The boy shot upright, blinking at the unexpected attention.

'Thorpe, Sir. Frank Thorpe.'

'Right, Frank Thorpe. You read next!' I was quite pleased with my authoritative tone.

Frank peered at me and then glanced down at his book, slowly picked it up and – by sheer chance – started reading at exactly the right spot. He ploughed on for a second or two, not knowing whether he had got it right or not, and then stopped after one sentence and looked up at me. We stared at each other, while the rest of the class stared at both of us. Gradually it dawned on Frank that he had got it right and a smile began to form.

I broke first. 'Nearly got you that time,' I said.

Frank took this in, but just for a moment. He put his book down on the desk and eyed me from under a shock of tousled hair.

'Yes, Sir. 'Nearly', Sir – but not quite. You see, I'm smarter than the average teacher!' (a phrase I vaguely remembered from an American cartoon film).

I should have been outraged at such insubordination, of course. There was a marked silence while the class took in a collective breath. Then I could hold it in no longer – I just guffawed. I thought it was genuinely funny. I started laughing uncontrollably. After a short pause the rest of the class joined in, even Frank himself. It was a priceless answer.

Frank was quite right. Most of the boys in that class were indeed 'smarter than the average teacher,' so I knew I had to be on my guard the whole time and I definitely had to give the impression at all times that I was certainly 'not average'. My resolve was tested immediately.

'What a goon!' I heard a high-pitched voice from behind me. It cut my laughter short and I swung around and pointed my finger at the culprit. Then I slowly lowered my hand when I saw that it was one of the only three girls in the class – elegant, classy, shapely and made-up to look ten years older. She was leaning back stretching her blouse tightly, head slightly on one side, obviously daring my next move. I changed tack.

'Now, young lady, I am pleased to meet you. And what is your name?' I spoke quietly and, I hoped, disarmingly. She was certainly not expecting this approach. She thought for a moment, but I hadn't given her any opportunity for a witty response.

'Lizzie' – (I raised one eyebrow) – '*Sir*,' she added.

'Lizzie, eh? That's not a proper name, is it?' I suggested. 'What name were you born with? Elisabeth with an 's', or Elizabeth with a 'z', or Lisa, or Elspeth? Which is it?'

Lizzie hesitated. She had been addressed as Lizzie for as long as she could remember. No-one had challenged her appellation before.

'With an 's' or 'z'. Whatever you like,' she answered eventually. 'No-one ever calls me Elizabeth anyway.'

I decided to carry on with the soft-soap approach, ignoring her initial provocation for now.

'Well,' I said in my smarmiest tone. 'we'll have to discover which, won't we, Elizabeth. That would be nice, wouldn't it?'

She shrugged her shoulders. 'If you like.' Lizzie didn't really care which letter it was since no-one used the name.

'It's a cissy name anyway – a bit like Clive, I always think.'

The boy next to her, who looked suspiciously as though he had his hand on her bare knee, sniggered sarcastically. This time my hand went up fast and straight and my finger pointed and wagged up and down menacingly, in a distinctly 'J'accuse' posture.

'And who might you be, then?'

He moved his head trying to stare into my eyes, aiming to communicate to me that he was not used to being treated in this manner, but I kept my finger wagging in front of his nose.

'Your name?'

'Paddy.' There was a marked Irish lilt and a noticeable grudging reluctance to engage in conversation. I sensed danger! Attack is the best form of defence being my credo, I raised my voice just a little.

'Paddy! That's not a proper name either, is it? You were baptised Patrick, weren't you?'

'Yes, but I don't use it.'

'Well you do in my class, Patrick. Shortening names is a form of idleness, and we will not tolerate idleness will we, Patrick? Eh?'

Before he could answer I leaned on his desk and peered straight at him.

'So, what is your name?'

'Patrick,' muttered Paddy very sotto voce.

'Louder!' I raised my voice.

'Patrick,' croaked Paddy.

'I can't hear you. Louder still!'

'PATRICK!' screeched Paddy.

'Cor blimey,' breathed a shocked voice from behind.

I swung round and pointed my still-wagging finger at the perpetrator. 'And you! Stand up, boy! What's your name?'

A little boy with large round spectacles shot up out of his chair.

'MICKRICK!' yelled the terrified youngster.

Collapse of the rest of the class. Victory for sir. I never had a moment's trouble from that class for the rest of the year.

Patrick, inevitably, became a minor punk rock star. Michael took over his father's wholesale fish company and Lizzie – she never did answer to Elizabeth except in my classes – well, she told me during the year that she had no intention and no need to do any homework or indeed any work at all.

'You see, Sir, I am going to be a model, an actress and then marry a lord'. And she did all three. The lord was forty years older than Lizzie and after eighteen months succumbed to the pace of her living and loving. At his funeral she is reported as saying: 'He died a very contented man, with a smile on his face.'

She put a smile onto many people's faces, did Lizzie. She and the rest of 4C taught me that teaching is a funny business and schools are funny places.

The Moving Finger of Time

This tale is a tribute to all those headteachers who can think on their feet, swivel in their chair, and keep a smile on their face.

I once knew a Head of a secondary modern school whose school was about to amalgamate with the local selective grammar school to become a comprehensive school. The new all-through school would be opening in new premises a mile away. The contest for the headship of this new school was between the two existing town Headteachers: the secondary modern Head and the grammar school Head.

The Chair and Vice-Chair of governors of the new school with two local authority school inspectors interviewed the two Heads separately in their own schools. Their role was to advise the governing body and the local education authority on which of the two Heads might make the best fist of being the Head of this new creature, a comprehensive school.

The inspectors were keen to draw out the educational philosophy of the two Heads and to enable them to explain to the governors their approaches to comprehensive education. They had listened to the grammar school Head's erudite and thorough analysis of curriculum reform, current developments in the theory of large school management, and the latest pupil behaviour management theory. All four now sat in front of Ken, the secondary modern Head. Behind Ken on the wall was a large, framed timetable, the week's periods neatly ruled in horizontal and vertical lines to make squares, each of which contained the names of classes, their teachers, and the rooms they occupied for each lesson, beautifully written in felt-tip pen, and all in glorious technicolour.

Eyeing this large and Picasso-esque work of art behind the Head's desk, the lead inspector, a lady with much experience of running comprehensive schools and a formidable reputation

14

in inspection circles, sought to get conversation going by pointing to it.

'This looks like a very impressive secondary modern timetable, Headmaster. Tell us, how you would transfer it to the new comprehensive school?'

She was rather pleased with herself – spotting a good ploy to lead into a discussion about the comprehensive school curriculum. She smiled at Ken and leaned back, waiting. This would demonstrate the depth of Ken's knowledge about comprehensive education and his understanding of the major shift that would be required from his secondary modern culture. She would be very interested in his answer, and would make sure the governors appreciated the importance, too. There was a moment of silence, and then a grin broke out on Ken's face. He swivelled round in his chair and stared up at the timetable.

'Ah, my secondary modern timetable. How would it transfer? Easy, really. You see, it's on four screws and I'll just unscrew it and take it over in my car.' He swivelled back and smiled again.

There was another moment of silence. The lady inspector squirmed in her chair.

'Err … err … actually … I did not mean … err … how you would physically move it … I meant…'

'It's all right,' laughed Ken, putting his hand out to stop any further embarrassment. 'I know what you meant. But I thought we were all a bit tense! Now, let's discuss not *what* we will teach at the new school, because that will largely be dictated by the National Curriculum and the teachers and students we already have. To me the important changes are going to be in *how* we teach and how *well* we teach. Our concentration should be on creating a powerful teaching force, don't you think?'

And so followed an hour of light-hearted but earnest banter about teaching styles, pupil attitudes, necessary resources, and essential training. All very satisfactory.

Ken got the new job. And the new school became one of the happiest amalgamations and the jolliest of places. Oh, and the old, framed timetable found a home – in the Head's private toilet, as a daily reminder!

Ken would often remark that whenever he felt he had got a bit above himself, or been a smidgen unfair to a colleague, he would slip into the loo 'for a good peer' – at his past.

Good Morning, School

Schools in the UK start the day with a mandatory act of collective worship, called traditionally 'morning assembly'. Although pupils often devise the content, it is traditional for the Head or a senior member of staff 'to take assembly', thus emphasising the importance and solemnity of the daily event. It is a ritual where all the school can see the Head in action, the pinnacle of the school's hierarchy. It can be a real joy, but sometimes, well …

When Marcus Brampton was teaching in a large inner-city school, he sometimes found himself with other Heads of Department supporting the Head at morning assembly in the Lower School, which consisted of Years 7 and 8 – eleven- to thirteen-year-olds. It was about a mile away from the Senior School, housed in what were once handsome and proud Victorian buildings right in the middle of the city, next to a crisp factory. Like its superior Edwardian senior building it had seen better days.

Teachers had to walk between the two buildings when scheduled to teach there. The Head, 'Johnny' Bloomer could drive there as he not only had a car allowance but also his name on the only parking space.

On Wednesdays Mr Bloomer would always take Junior School assembly in 'the other place'. He would take with him the prefect who was doing the obligatory Bible reading. Teachers continued to walk – or often run – to get there in time.

On the memorable occasion in question, Marcus was with his pal, Michael, at the back of the Junior School Hall with the other staff, some 200 juniors seated in front of them, not exactly straining their ears but silent and as attentive as eleven- to thirteen-year-olds can be in such circumstances. In the Lower School, boys sat on one side and girls on the other. And both ignored the other. Their eyes were on other things – like playing noughts and crosses or re-arranging the words of the hymn, or just dozing.

The Head and the sixth form prefect climbed up onto the stage. The prefect nipped over to the lectern housing the Bible. Act one of the morning entertainment began. The juniors, many of them boys with voices just breaking and others barely out of the growling stage, and girls not brave enough to drown the boys with their shrill soprano, and staff not yet awake enough to give full throat, together murdered another of Wesley's wonderful hymns, accompanied by an ecstatic Head of Music, Miss Hannah Dell, whose pounding of the organ was legendary. At the last note they all sat down, with a sigh and a clatter. Time to doze – time for the morning's Bible reading.

The duty prefect normally carried a note of the chapter and verses – except that on this occasion young Ricky Roberts, rushing too quickly over from the Senior School, did not. He fumbled in his pocket and could find no trace of it. But never mind, there would be a marker in the Bible, put there by the Head of Religious Education. It was always there – except that on this Wednesday morning it was not. Head of Religious Education, Gertrude Guest – Gospel Gertie to the kids, and most staff if the truth be told – had failed in the daily task because she arrived late and had just crept into the back of the hall.

Ricky only found out about the missing marker when the Head signalled to him to read and he grasped the lectern and the closed Bible. Sod's law was at work! No marker! He looked around wildly at the Head.

Now, Headmaster Johnny was ex-military, and seeing himself as the no-nonsense man of action, a leader of men – and women and prefects – strode across the stage, opened the Bible with a flourish, and pointed his finger. Read from there! It was quick, it was decisive – it was wrong!

The hapless prefect began to read.

'This morning's reading is,' he peered at the heading, taken from the Book of Ezekiel, Chapter 23.'

Lower school and staff subsided into the normal somnolence of morning assembly.

'The word of the Lord came again unto me, saying "Son of man, there were two women, the daughters of one mother: and they committed whoredoms in Egypt; they committed whoredoms in their youth …'

Marcus looked at Michael, who was staring straight ahead, refusing to look at his friend.

'… there were her breasts pressed …'

Marcus couldn't contain himself. 'Mike, this is going to be a day to remember!' Michael's mouth was twitching. Marcus could see he was trying desperately to keep control.

'… and there they bruised the teats of their virginity,' delivered in a totally deadpan voice. Ricky was in robotic mode.

Michael nearly fell off his seat, and usually drowsy colleagues were now waking up and taking note of a biblical reading, many for the first time in years.

Marcus thought, 'Johnny has got to stop it soon, surely,' even though it was obvious that Lower School had no idea what 'whoredoms' were, or what Aholah and her sister, Aholibar were up to – very often, it seemed – with a succession of captains, rulers, young men and horsemen riding on their horses. But Johnny made no move. He sat staring straight out to the front, over the tops of assembled heads, avoiding eye contact.

Young Ricky, still apparently impervious to the rustling amongst staff at the back of the hall, ploughed on. '… they lay with her and bruised the breasts of her virginity …'

Marcus turned to Michael, 'Johnny won't look at us – his eyes are closed.

'Probably died,' growled Michael.

Marcus spluttered. To be fair, he could not contain himself although he tried hard, turning the splutter into a simulated sneeze into his handkerchief. Gospel Gertie was also fanning herself with her hymn book, having given up trying to look as though she was engrossed in the lesson of the day. Marcus fancied she was no longer bothered that it was all her fault; *carpe diem* was now her philosophy. She wrung out her hankie and applied it to her face again.

'…. the Babylonians came to her in the bed of love and defiled her….'

Now even the Lower School Year 7 and 8s could not miss the beat of the 'B' in 'Babylonians', the 'b' in 'bed' and the 'd' in 'defile' in Ricky's reading. Heads shot up, eyes opened. Girls looked at girls with wonder and astonishment. The boys leered. What was clear was that no one, not staff, not pupils, not the Headmaster, had ever seen – or heard – anything like it. The whole audience was now awake and agog.

Little Sandra on the row in front of Michael and Marcus glanced sideways at her friend, and asked in a wondrous voice, 'Charmain – what do they use a file for then?'

Charmain looked at her pityingly, 'To get the chains off 'em. Babylonians use chains and things. It's well known.'

'Oh,' said Sandra in a small voice,'when did they put chains on them?'

'I don't know. In the war dome, I expect. Them Babylonians were always warring – it says so in what he's reading.'

'… They shall also strip thee out of thy clothes …'

'See,' said Charmain triumphantly, 'this war dome is a strip joint. They have chains there.'

'Ye gods,' Marcus muttered to no one in particular, but Welch from Chemistry heard him and muttered excitedly, 'Never enjoyed an assembly as much as this for twenty years. Bring it on.'

And Ricky Roberts did.

'… and I shall have thee naked and bare." And they went in unto her as they go in unto a woman that playeth the harlot …'

The rumble from the body of the hall began to reach a crescendo, mainly because the staff had given up trying to be composed and, unable to stifle laughter, guffaws and splutters, were just letting them rip. Those who were not bent double, had turned away and were weeping uncontrollably. It was not just the extraordinary reading, it was the look of bewilderment on most of the kids' faces. Some of the more worldly-wise had lost their dazed look, but most simply had no idea of what was happening.

Still the intrepid Head sat in solitary aloofness on the stage. He seemed to be in a trance. He clearly did not know whether to draw even more attention to the reading by leaping up and stopping it in his tracks, or just look thoughtful and at home with it all. In consequence he did nothing.

And, of course, in his decision-making mode at the outset he had failed to tell young Roberts where to stop. So, no instructions, no stopping. Ricky Roberts read the whole chapter – all 49 verses – by which time Johnny Bloomer had cut all ties with his colleagues, and indeed with normal life. The stage became his world, and he and Prefect Roberts its only inhabitants.

It was only when Ricky banged the Bible closed and declared, 'Here endeth the lesson,' that Headmaster Johnny sprang into life. He beckoned twelve-year-old Tabitha Gudgeon, Captain of Form 2G, to come onto the stage to read the prayer specially written by Gospel Gertie Guest for each daily assembly. However, when poor unsuspecting Tabitha was about to unfold her bit of paper, Gertie, just three seats away from Michael and Marcus, let out a strangulated gasp and clasped her hands to her mouth. 'Oh no …'

But, oh yes. Tabitha read out Gertie's prayer in beautifully clearly enunciated speech, written to follow the scheduled reading of the Book of Samuel Chapter 17, the story of David and Goliath, which Tabitha had spent the previous evening learning.

'We give thanks for today's uplifting story, and will seek to live by its example all the days of our life …'

PERIOD ONE: OPEN YOUR BOOKS

First Class

The start of the school year is a special time for families all over the world: lots of tears, cheers, hankies out. It's a rite of passage, but what are first days like – for teachers?

Francesca Luca was as British as they come, ie like every single person in the UK today she was from an immigrant family, in her case a fourth generation scion of immigrants from southern Italy, whose ancestor, Francesco De Luca hauled his family across Europe between the wars, en route for the United States, but got no further than Glasgow. Before he could find suitable berths for his young family, he had seen a niche for an importer of Italian pasta and started a small import business. Within a couple of years he had no need to go to the promised land across the pond, nor any desire either. He became more Scottish than many Scots, even rumoured to have worn a kilt on special occasions, indoors and without the dirk in his Royal Stewart stocking.

'He should have changed the name to MacLuca', his son Marco would joke to his children and then their children.

And so it came to pass that Francesca – 'Frankie' to everyone who got to know her – went through independent school education, to a top university and into teaching, another valuable bright physicist destined for a distinguished career as a university academic, but currently, as we meet her, a 'newly qualified teacher', an NQT, taking her first lesson at an East End of London comprehensive school.

Term had already begun when she got there some three weeks into September. She had followed her boyfriend to the big city when he had at last obtained a pupillage in barristers' chambers. Tagging onto prospective hubbies was the name of the game in those days.

Her first application had been snapped up with acute alacrity by the romantically, but inaptly named Lakeview

Community College. The lake, if it had ever been there, was now no more than a pond adjoining a huge abattoir. But that was by the way; it was a job, and the kids needed a teacher. Frankie was not the least fazed.

Her first lesson was with a Year 11 group.

'Not the top group,' said Guy Chapman, her Head of Department somewhat apologetically, 'it's Group E, full of youngsters who don't think that schoolwork is quite the place to show off their savoir-faire. I taught them last year and I would describe them as sharp rather than scintillating and cunning rather than clever – if you see what I mean.'

Frankie did 'see'. Some Glaswegians were not dissimilar; she had lived all her life in the middle of the city and had seen just about everything that inner city teenagers could throw in her path. But Year 11 Group E did not know that – what they saw was a dark-haired, brown-eyed, small and slender 'Miss', ripe for 'a bit of fun'.

'I am afraid the whole of Year 11 are studying 'Light' this week, Frankie. Not perhaps the best subject to start with, but we need to keep the large year group of 300 pupils roughly on the same track, and that's where we ended up last year as Year 10. We have to lighten their darkness about light all together.'

'Not a problem,' said Frankie, shrugging her shoulders. 'Light has to dawn at some point, so let it be now. Where are we with light?'

'Refraction. The lab technician will have set out all the apparatus. Everything's ready.'

So, there she was, standing in front of thirty boys and girls, all in school uniform, but needless to say, their own individual variations of it. Roughly ten were white, ten were Asian and Middle Eastern, and ten were black. There were sixteen girls and fourteen boys. Their names covered the nomenclature of both hemispheres and most continents. Roughly half of them could speak perfect English. The remainder could not, but by the astute arrangement of the school sat next to one of the English-speaking pupils, much the same as she had experienced on teaching practice.

After the usual pre-lesson greeting and mutual sizing-up, Frankie prepared to launch into an introduction to 'Light and Refraction'. She was stopped in her tracks by a voice from the back row.

'Are you going to try and teach us science, Miss?' The questioner looked around for adulatory support. She got a few giggles. The rest eyed Frankie, wondering how she would respond.

Frankie bent her head and appeared to be contemplating the question and how she would respond. She was actually glancing at the seating plan that the Head of Department had provided. 'This is how they had to sit in Year 10 so I expect them to just carry on,' he had told her. He had also written a few helpful notes against each name, such as: 'Gloria will have two buttons of her blouse undone – the rule is, only one.'

Frankie slowly lifted her head and glared at the girl at the back, the one with her blouse unbuttoned.

'No, Gloria. I am not going to 'try and teach you', I am *going* to teach you. but more importantly *you* are going to learn!'

Gloria's mouth dropped open.

'Cor, Miss, how did you know Gloria's name? Are you psychic?' asked the boy with his collar unbuttoned and tie loose, sitting next to the speechless Gloria.

Frankie smiled inwardly and held his gaze. 'Ah, Peter Pugliese, isn't it? Family originally from Calabria, I expect.' She nodded benignly at the equally dumbstruck Peter. His answer now came with much less insolent bravura.

'Yes, Miss, Peter. And yes, we did come from Calabria, a hundred years ago. How did you know that?'

Frankie was not going to tell him that she had his name on her sheet, and a note saying, 'sits next to Gloria, and will have his tie loose', nor was she going to reveal that she was passionately interested in all things Italian and had, by chance, once had a friend who was a member of the widespread Calabrian Pugliese family. But she tapped her nose instead.

'You should all know that I am a tip-top teacher. I belong to a secret spy-ring: **T**eachers **I**nformed **P**romptly when **T**aking

Over Pupils – TIPTOP.' She was quite pleased with that bit of improvisation. 'We know everything about you – and I mean everything!' Year 11 Science Group E did not know whether to laugh or take her seriously. This Miss was not proving to be as predictable as others.

Frankie bent her head to the desk again.

'Like you, Raj. You're a great cricketer, no? And you, Gary. You're on Arsenal's books, aren't you? Celeste, you are a cracking dancer, I believe.', They all stared in amazement. Peter was going to ask if there really was in fact a Tip-Top organisation but Frankie was not going to push her luck any further.

'Right, that's enough. Just remember, Miss knows all about you and this Miss is going to teach you whether you like it or not, so I suggest we all now get down to work. Today you are going to learn about the wonders of refraction. You have in front of you a board with pieces of equipment, batteries, bulb, stand with a card with a hole in it and another stand with a screen of white paper. You made circuits last year. Now you are going a step further. Look at the drawing I am going to chalk on the blackboard and then, in your pairs, build a circuit that will shine a light through the hole in the first piece of paper onto the white screen. Then we'll move on to something quite surprising even quite exciting. Let's see if you can do the build in five minutes.'

The class was happy enough to busy themselves building the circuit they had learned about in Year 10, beating the five-minute deadline. The last hand went up on the dot. Frankie handed out some new goodies.

'OK. That's good so far. I am now doling out a prism to each couple and I want you to position it between the card with a hole in it and the screen. Put it where you like and then move it to different positions. I want you to note what happens. Just that. Watch, take note and then record it in your exercise books and we'll discuss what you saw. Everyone understand?'

No dissenters.

'Good. Now, in order to see the effect clearly I'll switch off the lights for a couple of minutes.'

Frankie knew well that turning off lights with the blinds down was akin to offering your soul to the devil, but it had to be done. No compromises. With a deep breath and a silent prayer, she moved the switch. Fifteen little lights punctuated the darkness, and beams criss-crossed the benches, accompanied by inevitable cries of 'Oooh,' and 'I'm scared of the dark,' and 'I want to go home'. But the beams were bending and moving about – at least some of them were. Frankie was impressed.

'Hmmm, who'd have thought it would go this well?' she mused. then, as though they all had received a simultaneous order for blackout, every light went out, as if by magic.

Frankie's mood changed to one of disappointment and then angry determination. She pushed the switch back up and peered at each bench in turn. Not a single piece of apparatus remained on any bench: all fifteen bulbs, batteries, cards and stands had disappeared, not to mention all the ballpoint pens she had added to each collection. Vamoosed. She glowered at the class. Thirty shining, innocent faces beamed back at her. She felt herself becoming rather impressed by their ingenuity and prestidigitation. 'Quite brilliant,' she told her boyfriend later. But she was not going to admit that to them. Not yet anyway.

'So,' she thought, 'battle lines are drawn. It's them or me and it's definitely not going to be them. Here's a blow for equal rights – mine – and here's a challenge for teaching and learning: I am going to do the teaching and they are going to do the learning! They've heard me say that – now they're going to learn what it means.'

She had half-expected something to happen once darkness had fallen but hadn't fathomed out the detail. Now she knew. She had learned a thing or two on teaching practice in the Glasgow Gorbals area. She was not going to confront them. Nor was she going to let them taunt her or get her to plead for her belongings, or watch her squirm in any shape or form.

That's what they wanted, expected, and had achieved with other teachers – but they wouldn't do so with Frankie.

'I see you've given up work for the day, barely halfway through the period. Well, if that is the way you want it, that's fine. We'll spend the remaining forty minutes writing down the experiment and the results. I will dictate the experiment and the results – in very great detail. Oh, and we will now all have to return at the end of school and spend one-and-a-half hours doing the experiment again with the equipment you are so carefully preserving. And the Headmaster will pop in to take all your names so that he can inform your parents why you are all detained. Is that clear to you all?'

There was silence, except for the sound of dropping jaws. Gary was the first to put up his hand.

You can't do that, Miss. I have football practice immediately after school.'

'And I have to go for a dance class,' chipped in Celeste.

Frankie smiled sweetly at them. 'Well, you're going to have to find some way of explaining your absence to your very patient coaches then.'

She flashed her sweetest smile at them once again and turned away, signalling that she was not going to discuss the matter further.

'Now, open your exercise books and start writing. I will speak very slowly and will explain in minute detail what you would have seen. This may mean that we will not get everything done, even during the detention, so I'm afraid it might mean you having to come back tomorrow, too. It's such a shame, but it's your choice, not mine. We've already missed a couple more minutes of writing so let's start'

Before she could begin Peter thrust his hand up. Frankie thought that might happen. One of the scribbled notes told her that he shot off from school on the dot each day to help his dad in his grocer's shop during the post-school rush.

'All right, Miss. We can see you're a good sport. I reckon that if you switch out the lights for just one minute all the missing equipment will miraculously appear. How about it?'

Frankie was inwardly glowing. They were going to capitulate but they had to do it their way to keep face, as they saw it. Well, so be it. It augured well for the future. But she was not going to make it too easy for them.

'I can certainly do that, Peter, but you've wasted a lot of time, so we won't be able to get it all done by the end of the period – it looks as if we'll have to meet for at least half an hour after school. A pity, but it was not of my making.'

She detected a rustle of concern and discontent. The less militant were beginning to stir.

Gary thrust his hand up but was beaten to the question by an even faster Peter. 'Tell you what, Miss – how about us finishing off in the lunch hour?' His plaintive request was picked up by a number of others. They all looked expectantly at Miss, who was positively glowing with satisfaction at the way things were turning out. One more push and they would be hers!

'Very good suggestion Peter, and I can see ALL of you are in agreement. But ...' and here Frankie paused for effect. 'Hmm. The midday break is supposed to be time for me to recuperate, so I'm not sure.'

'Just this once, Miss,' pleaded Peter, followed by Gary and Celeste. 'Please, Miss.'

Frankie paused, contemplating her options, or so they thought. 'All right then.'

Smiles all round and a hint of a clap or two here and there.

'Thank you, Miss.'

'Great stuff.'

'That was a close one.'

Frankie held up her own hand this time. 'We are not going to finish it all in the half-hour at midday. So I expect the completed work to be handed to me tomorrow.' Groans went round the room. 'That's really not a lot to ask after what you've been up to, is it? So, let's use the next twenty minutes wisely, shall we? Starting now!'

First round went to Frankie, as did every other round that year. She heard Peter call her 'A top teach,' on one occasion, and that accolade meant as much to her as subsequent academic and national honours.

And that first lesson also stayed with her, especially and constantly remembered when she attended the biennial Year Group reunion, first as plain Mrs Birkett, then Dr Birkett, then Professor, and finally Lady Francesca Birkett, wife of His Honour Judge Norbert Birkett. But to Year 11 Science Class E, she was always just Miss.

Reach for the Sky

If you have ever considered what school life was like before the National Curriculum and GCSEs, Marcus Brampton's recollection during the 'Babbling Brook' reunion illustrates a familiar dilemma.

Before the advent of the National Curriculum and the General Certificate of Secondary Education (GCSE) in 1988, pupils in secondary schools took either GCEs (General Certificate of Education) at Ordinary level (known as the 'O Level') or the less academic CSEs (Certificate of Secondary Education). Some schools mixed both.

And so, before 1988 there was no prescribed national curriculum at all – except for Religious Education, which parents could opt their children out of. The only guide to the shape of any school curriculum was the general legal statement in the Education Act 1944 that the curriculum had to be 'broad and balanced'. This, combined with the whim of the Head and governors, the requirements of Further and Higher Education, and perhaps some input from the staff, led to each school having its own 'curriculum'.

The result was that the most academic students took GCEs at Ordinary Level or Advanced Level; the less academic took CSEs, for which you could choose to use the Mode 1 route (an end-of-course examination) or a Mode 3 route, which was via courses determined and examined by the school and moderated by the CSE Board. Or the school could choose the Mode 2 course and examination which was a kind of amalgamation of Modes 1 and 3.

Mode 3 courses at the majority of schools were usually, but not always, created by the staff for youngsters who had the most difficulty in learning and who needed all the help the staff could give to feel some pride in their efforts. There grew a strange but laudable tradition of calling Mode 3 courses 'Studies': Computer Studies, Rural Studies, Design Studies, Motor Vehicle Studies, Housecraft Studies, Citizenship Studies – the list was endless. They usually depended for success on the enthusiasm, dedication and predilection of the member of staff who had devised them, taught them and persuaded an Examination Board to examine them and award certificates.

It may now seem a bit 'Heath Robinson', just playing around with the notion of testing knowledge and skill, but actually for many pupils in many schools it instilled a notion of success. They could learn to learn, find out things from different sources, talk and write about them, and actually excel at something while learning something useful on the way.

What happened in 1988, when the GCSE replaced the former CSE and O Level qualifications, was that a large tranche of pupils lost the opportunity to get a top grade. The uniting of GCE and CSE did, of course, theoretically allow access to the full range of grades to all students, but in practice it was an arrangement designed by the elite for the elite, ie those with some academic bent, even if only a modicum. It did nothing for those who had no such bent. The old 'Studies' disappeared and so, if you examine the history carefully, did opportunities for a many technical, skills-based youngsters. Hence the gross skill shortage successive governments are always lamenting, which was self-inflicted, but there we are. Not many politicians, especially influential ones, had come up through the CSE ranks.

But back to those CSE days. Alarm bells used to ring if a school had a very particular and peculiar 'Studies' course devised by a member of staff with a specific skill and that member of staff left! Woe, woe! And thrice woe!

It happened at my school once upon a time when the then Head of Maths, who had been a jet fighter pilot in a previous life, ran a Mode 3 Aeronautics Studies course. The courses were two years long and, because of his knowledge and experience as a Tornado pilot, the Aeronautics course was a great hit with his class. Lots of insight, personal stories, model-making, spotting-days, visits to aerodromes – stirring stuff.

But with painful inevitability he left, with one group about to move into the examination year.

My senior colleague in charge of Mode 3 CSE courses, Never-say-die Neville, did not take long before plonking himself in front of me on that memorable day when we learned that our pilot was flying away.

Nev eyed me silently. 'Headmaster …' he began slowly. Now, he never called me 'Headmaster' unless something ominous was about to follow that was not to my advantage.

'Y-e-s, Deputy Headmaster?' I countered.

'Headmaster, we cannot possibly ask a new member of staff to take on Aeronautical Studies. And I am fairly certain that there isn't much chance of persuading you to advertise for an airline pilot to come and teach here, is there?'

'Not much chance,' I agreed.

'Right then, Headmaster!' He sat down and leaned forward over the desk. 'Here is the textbook for this course.' He said this while extracting from his jacket pocket a slim book. He waved it in front of me.

'It is, Headmaster, the Ladybird Book of Aeroplanes.

'That's it?' I asked querulously, secretly knowing full well that it was.

'It is, Headmaster. This plus any photos of aeroplanes that you may have lying around. Oh, and a few made-up tales of derring-do over Iraq, perhaps. You will forgive me, I hope, for ruining your weekend but I am afraid it's either me or you.'

I feared as much. It was, of course, inevitable fair game. My heart sank and I felt for a brief moment like telling him it was his job to ensure the Mode 3 courses were fulfilled – which contractually, it was. However, reason and good staff relations prevailed. I knew I could not pull rank! Nev had been a colleague for some fifteen years and was a dear friend. We knew each other well. I couldn't let a few aeroplanes get between us.

So, I eyed him back. My brain was whirring. I decided to let the wheel of fortune roll. I was sure he would both appreciate this and be amused by it, wouldn't he?

'OK. There's only one solution Nev between gentlemen. Let's toss for it,' I suggested. I have to admit that I hoped he might say 'Oh no, Headmaster, I'm happy to sacrifice myself.'

He did not!

'I have a coin right here, Headmaster.'

So we tossed for it, and the gods were with me that day. Poor Nev. The moment the coin stopped spinning and fell tails up, he became the school's instant aviation expert and finished the year with total recall of the *Ladybird Book of Aeroplanes*. To this day I owe him!

I could have told him my father had served in Burma in the RAF during the Second World War as an aeroplane engineer. And that I had all my father's old notes and a large number of photos of old Blenheims and Mosquitoes in the jungle airfields. But I didn't. Sometimes one's courage is called on once too often. I have prayed for forgiveness since then. But my penance has been never to forget my pedagogical cowardice.

Anyway, Nev did very well with both the course and the group, but then Nev did well with everything and rightly went on to a Headship – not, I hasten to add, that this had anything to do with knowledge of aeroplanes. It was after all a Headship on the east coast – a course in Fishing Studies would have been more relevant! And there was a *Ladybird Book of Coarse Fishing*!

Making Ends Meet

My first teaching post, said Marcus, was at a school in Croydon. In 1961 my starting salary, even with the London weighting, was just £525 per year – about £40 per month after deductions. In order to pay our rent and then our mortgage, I had to supplement our income, and I did this by teaching evening classes a couple of times a week at the local Further Education College. The lessons were to young apprentices, who had to take compulsory Use of Literacy courses as part of their professional certification. I am not sure what the presumption was: that plumbers and electricians ought to be literate, which is a reasonable aim, or that the course ought to have some academic underpinning, which is outrageously condescending.

Whichever it was, a worthy or unworthy aim, you will not be surprised that the vast majority every year did not want anything to do with it. On the other hand, they were more than happy to show their displeasure in the usual ways – too painful for me to recount now, or even recall!

It was certainly vital for me to grab their interest, even if for only a few minutes of the hour-long sessions. Why? Well, simply because I needed the money, and I needed the Use of Literacy course to continue and me to be its tutor. My first group turned out to be much the same as the ones that followed.

The immediate task, it seemed to me, was to improve their grammar, spelling and punctuation – not the most attractive of missions for educating plumbers, electricians and bricklayers. They were not taken in by my claim that they would benefit by being able to write a good job application or a polite request for a client to pay an outstanding bill. 'We've got our own ways for those,' they told me. 'We've never had any problem getting people to understand us.'

'Well, you have to attend the course or you won't get your professional certificate, so how about treating it as a challenge, then? Achieving something you have never managed before?' That appealed to them. Much more attractive.

'Right,' said Lenny the Ladder, an apprentice scaffolder, 'I'll give it a go, but only so long as you don't bore the pants off me, right?' Lenny was fond of adding 'Right' to all his pronouncements. It gave them an earthy gravitas. And he was such a leader that all the others began to emulate him. The class rebounded with 'rights'.

'Right, Lenny,' I countered, 'it's a deal.' The rest of the group, nineteen rather well-built late teenage blokes and one equally well-built female bloke, a trainee woodworker, fell in line.

I strained hard, very, very, hard to make it fun. A joke here, a mystery there, laughter everywhere – anything to disguise the fact that I was on a knife edge.

We all trod gingerly round the edges of what they on the one hand saw as a terribly boring exercise of pure learning, and me, on the other hand, well, what I clutched at was an indispensable provider of income!

The technique that appealed to them most – to my surprise – was my invention of the 'the cat sat on the mat' routine, the learner's easy guide to learning punctuation and sentence construction.

To illustrate this: their most common error, stemming from their lack of basic understanding of the vagaries of English grammar (and this is true of many teenagers today, too), was to sprinkle commas, or no punctuation at all, where full stops should have been applied. I attacked this head on.

I used 'The cat sat on the mat. It lapped its milk.' to demonstrate the use of a full stop, which could only be got rid of by a joining word 'and' or 'but' or by making one of the sentences into a clause, not a sentence: 'When the cat sat on the mat, it lapped its milk.' or 'Before the cat sat on the mat, it lapped its milk.' It was a last throw, an act of desperation.

Unaccountably they cottoned on to this – in their own inimitable way! First, they demanded to know the name of the cat. Right. Fair enough.

I thought of 'Sam', since my family had once looked after a friend's Siamese 'Sam', which had ripped my shirt to pieces when I had offered it tinned cat food instead of salmon, a delicacy Sam had grown up on. Sam was not going to compromise!

But my lads, and girl, rejected that immediately, simply because one of them had a girlfriend, Sam. Right. Fair enough.

They threw out more: 'Tabby', 'Orlando', 'Moggy' (that got close to acceptance, but two carpenters considered that 'our cat' deserved a better name), 'Felix'. No, too corny. Right. Fair enough.

We eventually hit, unanimously, on 'Figgy'. Why? Simply because one apprentice plumber, Luigi, announced that he had had a cat called Figaro. His plumber dad was mad keen on Mozart's operas – after Verdi's and Puccini's. He was especially fond of *The Marriage of Figaro*. That did it. The rest of the class consented, I suspect because they were utterly bewildered by the reason, totally fed up with coming up with more names, and Luigi was even bigger than Lenny.

So, for the rest of the ten-week term they made up hundreds of versions of 'the cat' and 'the mat', and why it 'sat'. And they loved it. I did not know why then and I do not know why now.

I had to incorporate the two sentences into everything I taught them. If I went on too long at some other exercise, they would demand to know if my cat was ill or was stuck on the mat! So, I used this for evermore in my teaching – at the college and at every school in which I taught. I usually ended with a challenge for the longest correctly punctuated sentence, which did not use the same word twice (except for the definite and indefinite articles and words of two letters). Everywhere I went it was a hit. The most imaginative response to the exercise was by a smart eleven-year-old (now, by the way, an eminent professor):

When the cat had at last seen fit to sit down, having found a convenient mat on which to perform this deed, and after having discovered milk, which had been placed in a bowl, she, or possibly 'he', decided that it might be delightful to consume the said liquid as quickly as possible, and so the feline practised a lapping movement with its tongue, which turned out to be just right for the task in hand, or paw, so that it very soon finished all the beverage, leaving it with a satisfied look on its face, and a great deal of whiteness around the mouth.

I never got any longer ones that were correct in every respect. I just wish it had been a carpenter or plumber – that would have been a real coup!

Tripping over Triplets

A Headmistress friend once told me about her frustrating but enlightening experience of having identical twins, two-thirds of triplets, in the school for seven years. I was interested because I had a similar experience in my school. My colleague wrote down her thoughts for me.

Knowing which child is which ought to be easy enough but, in the case of identical twins, other rules and forces come into play.

This happened at my school when the A B C Twist triplets joined us and stayed for the next seven years. Colin was easy enough to spot – he was a boy and from the start he went his own way. Angela and Barbara were impossible! They were in every way identical. Their mother could tell them apart. I was not so sure that dad could all the time, but I and my colleagues certainly could not at any time. I asked the parents at one point whether the girls could wear something to distinguish them.

'Well, Headmistress, it's you who insists on uniform and I am not going to allow my daughters to be singled out for discriminatory treatment.'

'Can't one wear a badge with a capital A and one with a capital B?'

'Only if every other child has a badge with the capital letter of their first name.'

I could see her point, but I was not going to change the dress code for a thousand pupils just to ease this singular problem, which would go away in seven years. Seven years! Something had to be done!

Perhaps the girls would be prepared to help?

No. The girls were adamant that they were who they were, and the staff must address them as best they could. Maybe, Angela suggested – or was it Barbara? – that the staff might

41

attend 'person recognition training', something like an aeroplane recognition course? My colleagues were not persuaded.

I told the staff that we just had to do our darnedest to distinguish. No ifs, no buts, just get on with it, and I disappeared back into my office and shut the door – pretty well for the next six years.

For nearly the whole of the first year we stumbled away, invariably addressing A as B and B as A and apologising when we got it wrong. We tried invoking brother Colin's aid as the supra-triplet, but he was no use at all: he just knew which was which but did not know why he knew which was which

We then found that neither Angela nor Barbara minded being wrongly addressed. We did not have to apologise. If we addressed 'Angela' she answered as Angela, even if she was Barbara. And if we addressed Angela as Barbara, she would smile sweetly and say, 'Yes, what is it, Miss? But by the way, I am Angela.'

And we further discovered that it did not matter, because everything they did was, well, the same. Admittedly any essays or stories or art pieces would be different in detail, but the general content was the same. They would get the same mark in Maths or Science tests, the same marks for English or History essays. They ran the 100 metres in the same time and jumped the same height at the high jump. And when Angela played Hermione in *A Midsummer Night's Dream*, Barbara played Helena – and they understudied each other's role, of course. Colin refused to take part at all!

When it came to choosing GCSE subjects, they chose the same ones. And when the results came out Angela had nine grade As and a B, and Barbara had nine grade As and a B, and yes, the B was in the same subject. Meanwhile Colin, in his drive to be different, only took five of the same subjects as his sisters but still got nine grade As and a B.

I interviewed all three for their sixth form Advanced Level choices and was not the least surprised that the girls chose the same subjects. Colin chose three entirely different ones. At the

42

start of their final year, I also chatted to them again separately about their university and undergraduate subject choices. Lo and behold, for the girls, the same university, and the same subject. Colin went off on his own.

I am usually very placid, not given to excessive frustration, but I felt I really had to confront them with the folly of their doing every single thing together. I decided I had a duty to challenge them. So, I sent for them to call on me together. They sat primly in front of my desk. I took a deep breath.

'Angela?' I said. Not a flicker. I could be right; I could be wrong. I turned to the other. 'Barbara?' No flicker there either. 'Look, surely there must come a time when you branch out on your own without doing exactly the same as your twin? And surely going on to university is just the time to make your own way in life?'

No doubt I could have done it better, but I thought I had made my point. They sat silently for a moment and then both started to speak together.

'Headmistress, we hear.' They stopped together and the right-hand twin held out a hand to the other. 'Angela will speak first, Miss.' Angela did.

'Headmistress. Please do not patronise us. We are individuals. We make our *own* decisions, in our own time, and we've done this all our lives.'

Barbara took over.' You see, Headmistress, we never discuss our decisions; our decisions just happen to coincide, and surely you do not expect us to change our decisions just because they are the same?'

'Well, no, I suppose not.' I had never thought of it that way!

So, of course they went to the same university, and of course got the same degree in the same subject. However, they did go on to marry different husbands, but both produced sets of identical girl twins. They are not due to come to this school, I am told.

Colin is a much-respected child psychologist.

Shall I Compare Thee to a Summer's Day

There are times when teaching and learning come together in glorious synchronicity – not pre-planned, not deliberately sought, just there, all of a sudden. The learner realises that knowledge and ideas are percolating through; the teacher knows that learning is taking place. Such lessons cannot be sabotaged by a determined – or plain awkward – student, or be side-tracked by competing interests.

Rachel Duffy told Marcus of one particular Lower Sixth A Level English lesson on a glorious summer morning which took on a momentum of its own, radiating edification and entertainment – for all.

Rachel began her lesson brightly, full of the confidence that knowledge of the subject, love of literature, and particular delight in reading Shakespeare, engender.

'Now, Lower Sixth A, this bright sunny morning we are going to study a short poem by Shakespeare that is in your anthology, but I don't want you to open your book just yet. Sit back and listen to it.'

The Lower Sixth English group of sixteen-/seventeen-year-olds settled down in all their familiar poses. Rachel read Sonnet 18 with due emphasis on the conversational rhythm and the poet's wit:

Shall I compare thee to a summer's day?
Thou art more lovely and more temperate.
Rough winds do shake the darling buds of May,
And summer's lease hath all too short a date.
Sometime too hot the eye of heaven shines,

And often his gold complexion dimmed;
And every fair from fair sometime declines,
By chance, or nature's changing course, untrimmed;
But thy eternal summer shall not fade,
Nor lose possession of that fair thou ow'st,
Nor shall death brag thou wand'rest in his shade,
When in eternal lines to Time thou grow'st.
So long as men do breathe, or eye can see,
So long lives this and this gives life to thee.

When she had finished, the class was silent. She could see they were struck by it, but were not sure why.

'So, what are your first thoughts, Cynthia? What is Shakespeare saying and to whom?'

Cynthia, the obvious choice for a first attempt as she had proved to be the most sensitive reader and had already indulged in her own poetry writing, sat up and smiled.

'I think it is beautiful, Miss. Shakespeare is obviously in love with this woman.'

'Hey up, our Cynthia. How do you know it is a woman, eh?' Siggy, Siegfried Bluhm to his parents, had made his first strike. 'It doesn't say it's a woman. He could be writing to a bloke.'

Cynthia bridled. 'Don't be daft, Siggy. Would Shakespeare call a man "lovely"?'

'He might. He could be gay. Perfectly possible. You obviously haven't read any gay poetry.'

'Yes I have, and it's nothing like this. My friend Belle writes gay poems.'

'What! Isabelle in Year 11? Blimey, I'm going to a gig with her on Friday! She's not gay is she?'

'I didn't say she was! I just said she wrote poems about gay people and things.' Cynthia was getting flustered.

Rachel considered it time to intervene. 'Okay, okay. That's enough. We're discussing poems of 1607 not Belle of Year Eleven.'

'That's a rhyme, Miss. Well done! A cue for a poem, I think.' A voice piped up from the back of the class, where Keith

Kingdom was leaning back against the lockers. Keith was the class observer, the MI5 undercover agent, George Smiley of Lower Sixth English, working in the shadows and ready to strike if he thought the cat needed putting among the pigeons.

He launched forth.

It was the year of Our Lord 1607,
And Shakespeare was in seventh heaven.
He'd pulled a Dark Lady,
And a bloke, rather shady,
But he'd missed out on Belle of Year Eleven.

Laughter, and then clapping and a few whistles from the rest of the class. Rachel gave him a wan smile and a little nod of acknowledgement. She admired Keith's ability to knock off witty ditties at will. They were always pointed, relevant, and funny, a refreshing change from the introspective moanings of much of modern music, she thought. Keith had his own group and wrote both lyrics and music. In common with most contemporary pop music, you couldn't hear the words when accompanied by the thump of the drums and twangs of guitars, but Keith always surreptitiously left a handwritten copy on Rachel's table. He was highly intelligent and talented with it, but he did like stirring things up if he could. She reckoned that Keith Kingdom and The IsamBards might have a bright future if Keith could keep it up.

'Thank you for that, Keith. But let's get back to the seventeenth century and Shakespeare's sonnet, because that is what it is. I have to say, Cynthia, that actually Siggy is probably right. This is Sonnet 18 in a whole volume of over 150 sonnets and it is right in the middle of the sonnets addressed to some mysterious man. There is a reference to a W H on the title page of the first collected edition. We don't know if it is this man being addressed in Sonnet 18, or some other, or, indeed, whether it is the woman he addresses in over a hundred of the later sonnets. She is often referred to as the Dark Lady of the Sonnets.'

46

'So it could be the Dark Lady he is making eyes at here.' Cynthia was not about to give in. 'It could have been slipped in here. Much more likely, if you ask me.'

'We're not asking you,' muttered Siggy ungraciously. 'Whoever it is, Miss, it doesn't alter the words, or what he's saying, does it?'

'No, that is true.' Well worked out, Siggy, she thought.

Siggy kept going. 'Anyway, why do you say it is written by Shakespeare, Miss? It might not be written by Shakespeare. You've told us that some people think he didn't write the plays, so he might not have written these poems either.'

Rachel had the first pangs of a sinking feeling. She had to get control of the discussion or they would never get round to the amazing subtlety of the language and all that is gloriously positive about English poetry.

'Siggy, we know it is by Shakespeare, because the first edition was printed in 1609 and says it is Shakespeare's sonnets. Doesn't that sound good enough?'

'That doesn't prove anything, Miss. You told us that people in Shakespeare's time often pinched each other's works and Shakespeare didn't bother to have his plays published in his lifetime, did he? So why would he bother to publish poems?'

Rachel detected a rustle of restlessness in the class.

'Can't we get on, Miss,' whispered Bronwen, normally hidden behind others and generally silent.

'Good idea, Bronwen. Let's just call him "the poet". It doesn't matter whether it is William Shakespeare or not. We still have the poem.'

As soon as she said it she knew it was the wrong call.

'Not matter, Miss?' It was Siggy again. 'I would have thought it mattered a lot. We're studying Shakespeare for A Level, not some mysterious poetry-writing narcissistic ghoul!'

'All right! It's definitely Shakespeare!'

Rachel felt her voice getting a little strident and tried to rein it in.

'Your A Level poetry anthology says it is by Shakespeare, just as it says there are poems by Donne, Milton, Pope,

Wordsworth, Tennyson and others. If the Exam Board thinks it is by Shakespeare, then it is by Shakespeare. Right?' She did not wait for an answer. 'Open your books now at the poem Sonnet 18 and have a look at it.'

Rachel sensed that Siggy was about to take issue with this simple request so she added quickly, 'And when you have read it through, we can discuss it.' She watched the group bend their heads over the text. Very satisfying. She never had any problem with this group as far as interest went. They were keen to learn, and argue. For some, notably Siggy, the arguing came before the learning. But there was never a dull moment, that's for sure.

'Olive, what are your first thoughts?' Olive was thoughtful and careful. She could be relied on not to say anything outrageous that might get Siggy going again.

'If he is addressing his patron, miss, and trying to butter him up, then I'm not sure about the "lovely" bit. Would you really try to please another man by calling him "lovely", especially if the patron is an old man with a lot of money?'

Rachel wondered how they had managed to become so fixated on this one word, not one she had given much thought to when she was preparing the lesson. She was beaten to a reply, once again, by Siggy.

'That's my point! It isn't to his patron at all! It seems to me more likely that he was trying to get off with one of the actors.'

There was a distinctly uncomfortable murmur around the class at this. Siggy, oblivious, ploughed on. 'Look, all the actors in Shakespeare's time were male, and it's well known that all actors are luvvies!'

An even more anxious murmur now. But Siggy was racing down his tangent. 'Yes, I see it now. It's a subtle hint to one of his mates, probably one of the younger actors who used to play the female parts. 'Thou art more lovely and more temperate.' It's a definite call to come up to his place and study his collected poems, if you see what I mean!'

'Siggy! Stop there! All actors are not luvvies.' Rachel decided she had to cut him short. 'That is not a fair remark. I'll grant you that it certainly suggests that the man is a young man. He probably wouldn't call an older man 'lovely', that's true. But does it matter who it is?'

Rachel was hoping that she could get them round to discussing how the sonnet form is handled, the way the wheedling tone is created, the extraordinary ability to make such a tight poetic form as a Petrarchan sonnet seem like effortless spoken conversation. But Siggy wasn't finished yet.

'It matters to the actor he's addressing, Miss. And it matters to Shakespeare, too! He doesn't want any hoary old luvvy getting the wrong idea and knocking on his door, and crawling all over him, does he?'

'Siggy, I know you are sincere about wanting to understand the poems we read, but could you just accept for one moment that Shakespeare is addressing some unknown person that he wants to praise' (she put up her hand here to stop Siggy muscling in), 'for whatever purpose, and whoever it is, and concentrate on how he uses the poetic form and language to do it?'

She paused and picked out Bronwen. 'What do you notice about the language of the poem, Bronwen?'

Bronwen traced a couple of lines with her finger. 'It's not like poetry, not like sort of flowery music is it?' She looked up at Rachel, not sure whether she was making a fool of herself, or not. Rachel smiled and nodded encouragingly. Bronwen continued. 'It seems as though Shakespeare the poet is talking to us in a normal speaking voice.' She looked up again.

'Excellent, Bronwen! Well noticed.'

At last we can get back on track, thought Rachel. 'In my view all great English poetry uses what

49

you might call "ordinary speech". Chaucer, Shakespeare, Donne, Wordsworth.' She wanted to move on to discussing how the choice of words, the length of line, the rhythm, the imagery, were all used to create the tone and full meaning of the poem. It was not to be.

'What about Milton? You haven't mentioned him, Miss. My mum says he is the greatest English poet. *Paradise Lost* and *Paradise Regained*. Great stuff so my mother says. Why haven't you included him?'

Rachel pushed her hand through her hair. She respected Siggy's mother, a lecturer in Classics at the university, but as far as Rachel was concerned Milton was not really in the main speaking-voice tradition that she found so rewarding. But was it wise to start another hare running? If she weakly caved in and said 'Yes, I include Milton,' she would be untrue to herself. She sighed inwardly. 'I have not included Milton, great as he is, Siggy. Because he was more in the tradition of the ancient Greek and Roman poetry of poets like Homer and Vergil. You had to be very well educated, even very learned, to be able to engage with Milton's poetry and still do. That is why he's not widely read these days. I commend your mother for her support of him.' That should do the trick, she thought. She hoped.

'An amorphous heap of pseudo knowledge.' A voice intoned from the right under the large windows where the sun continued to shine its light on the class.

Hello, thought Rachel. Ernie is up to it again! Faroukh will follow shortly, I'll bet my life on it! Sure enough Ernie's neighbour leant forward.

'Quite right, Ernie, nothing but a khamsin of ecclesiastical mongering.'

Rachel put her elbow on the table and cupped her chin in her hand. She knew from previous encounters that the two friends liked to make up an outrageous phrase and then challenge each other to get them into a class discussion. If they decided they had agreeably agitated Miss they awarded themselves a high five. She knew very well what they were doing.

At first she had been totally thrown by their peculiar air of serious literary criticism, but she had never told them to stop it. If being egregiously witty grabbed them, then it grabbed her as well. They had excelled themselves this time, she thought – two phrases! Rachel had a choice now. She could just smile knowingly at them and offer them her own metaphoric high five and move on as she normally did or challenge them for an explanation. Hmm. Best get on, she thought – no, maybe not, that is what they expect. They ought to be put on the spot sometimes. Here goes. She straightened up and pointed at Faroukh.

'Who are we talking about here, Faroukh? Shakespeare or Milton?'

'Oh, goodness me, Miss, Milton, of course! You wouldn't call Shakespeare "amorphous" or "pseudo" or "an ecclesiastical monger" now would you?'

'So, Faroukh, explain to us why Milton's poetry is as you describe.'

Faroukh did not answer immediately. Rachel could detect his mind going into overdrive. He was not expecting to have to justify himself.

'I haven't actually read *Paradise Lost*, Miss – who has? But we Jains don't believe in one creator god, you know. In our religion we have a number of gods and we don't believe the world was created by anybody. It just exists, see? So it's not surprising that I think, like Ernie, that all Milton's meanderings are pseudo? Isn't that so, Ernie?'

Ernie was not expecting his friend to pass the buck. 'Er, well, er—'

'Yes, Ernie, do explain it to us. We are all agog with anticipation.' It was Keith from the shadows of the back of the room. He was smiling sweetly at a flummoxed Ernie.

Ernie ignored the interruption and addressed Rachel. 'Well, Miss. Faroukh and me, we've been giving this some thought.'

51

Rachel could not let this pass. 'But, Ernest, Faroukh just said that you haven't read *Paradise Lost.*'

'Ah, not the whole of it, Miss, but we have read a bit. And Faroukh and me don't think he's following the Bible story anyway. Do we, Faroukh?'

Faroukh wasn't playing. He waved airily at his friend. 'You're doing very well, Ernie. Carry on.'

Ernie stared at his pal and then round the class. 'As I was saying, we, that is Faroukh and me, we have noticed that Milton doesn't even mention the name of Jesus in ten books. He's just peddling his own version, so it's fair to say the poem is "amorphous' and "pseudo". That's my – our – view.'

'Congratulations, Ernie! Fancy being able to reach that profound conclusion about *Paradise Lost* without reading it.'

'Er, well, as I said, not all of it, not quite. I mean, it's more than 10,000 lines. Life's too short! But I've read a synopsis, Miss. And I did start reading the first book. But when you see that it takes sixteen lines to write the first sentence, just to say that he is going to describe "man's first disobedience", and twenty-six lines to tell us he is going to "justify the ways of god to man", then I think it is reasonable to lift your eyes to heaven, if you see what I mean. You know you're in for the long haul. Your life is not going to be in the fast lane! But I tell you what, Miss. Shakespeare would have taken at most just two lines to tell us what he was up to.'

Ernie was beginning to warm to his defence now. Rachel admired his growing skill. But before she could cut things short, Keith's voice came from the shadows. Straight in there.

Of man's first disobedience I'll let you know,
You'll hear about it all from the upstart crow.

There you are, Miss. Two lines. Sorted.'

More persistent rustling from the rest of the class. Some chuckles, a few groans.

'Do we have to sit through all this, Miss? Can't we get on with Sonnet 18? It's much more interesting.' This from Greta, usually silent on any issue unless pressed.

'OK, Greta. Let's get back to Shakespeare. But thanks Keith. I admire the way you can invent lines just like that, and thanks Ernest and Faroukh for your Miltonic interlude. Greta, tell me your thoughts.'

'Well, Miss. I've been looking at the rhymes.'

'There's only one rhyme!' Siggy was back, clearly thinking he had been left out for far too long. 'The last two lines.'

'What are you on about, Siggy?' Greta was indignant. 'The whole poem is rhymed. Just look ABAB CDCD EFEF GG.'

Siggy bent down and peered at the text.

'Blimey, you're right, Greta. It sounded so natural when Miss recited it. I never gave rhyme a thought. How cool is that!'

Siggy traced the lines in the text. 'It's got a rhyme scheme and all the lines are ten syllables. Yet it sounds just as if he is talking to this W H chap, or whoever it is. Are all one-hundred-and-fifty-four sonnets like that, Miss?'

'Yes, Siggy, every one. Extraordinary isn't it? All the same, yet all of them different.' Rachel explained further. 'Shakespeare constructed his sonnets in the style of the fourteenth-century Italian poet, Petrarch – fourteen lines, rhyming just as Greta had noted. A few years after Shakespeare John Milton – I'm sure Ernie and Faroukh know this – used a variant. Still fourteen lines, but in two halves, an octet and a sestet, rhyming ABBAABBA and then CDECDE.'

'Hey!' This was Faroukh interjecting. He had stopped leaning against the radiator and was now leaning forward holding two books, one in each hand. 'I'm having another look at this extract from *Paradise Lost*. Seems as if Milton also wants a private chat with us, but he's talking to his learned university mates, I reckon. He says it is his "Heavenly Muse" who is singing, not him personally. But Shakespeare just calls his poem "this".'

No one said a word. Faroukh looked up. 'I thought that was interesting.' He shrugged his shoulders and looked rather apologetically at his classmates.

'Faroukh, I think we are all quiet because we are thinking about what you said, and we do not have the Milton in front of us.' Rachel was impressed by Faroukh's obvious engagement with the poetry. 'But I have to say, I think you are making a very good point of comparison, or perhaps, contrast, between the way the two poets use language. They are both writing for audiences they know and know how to address. I am so glad you have noticed that. Now, getting back to Sonnet 18, what are your thoughts, Jamie?'

Before timid Jamie could open his mouth, a different voice cut in – Kaye, who was another one who was usually intimidated by the stronger characters in the group, and never said a word if she could get away with it.

'Oh, I think I have cracked it, Miss. He starts with – what's it? – a rhetorical question. He asks if he should compare this person to a summer's day but he is going to anyway so he doesn't wait. He says he would do so, but the person he is addressing is more lovely than the summer, more balanced, "temperate". That's a compliment. And then he butters up the man, or woman if you prefer, by saying that his "eternal" summer will never fade, because it will be kept fresh in this poem. Is that right, Miss?'

Rachel was once again impressed, not just by the simple exposition, but by the fact that Kaye had felt moved enough by the poem to want to say something about it. She did not have to say whether she liked it or not. Her engagement with it was clear to everyone.

'Well expressed, Kaye. You've sorted it out in your mind really well.'

Keith came back again. 'Not only are the lines all ten syllables, Miss, they are all based on that iambic thing you explained to us – SHORT/LONG, SHORT/LONG, tee tum, tee tum, tee tum – but he doesn't bother keeping strictly to it. He's more interested in suggesting that he is having a private conversation. Well, not a conversation, perhaps, more trying on a bit of smarm. Look how he uses long languorous words and syllables in the first line to bamboozle the reader into thinking this is going to be a conventional love poem. And then he changes tack completely at the start of the second line with a thumping "Thou'". And the mood has changed, and the rhythm of the line has changed.'

Rachel was open-mouthed. 'Have you just thought that up, Keith?'

'Not the gist of it, Miss, I have to admit. My mum and dad and me actually we were discussing it last night. But it has all become a bit clearer this morning. I can see now how Shakespeare manipulates our feelings by modulating the rhythm. We were talking about modulation at the County Orchestra practice last Saturday. You can do it with words as well as music. I see that now.'

Before Rachel could reply, Kaye continued. 'Everyone knows the line "Rough winds do shake the darling buds of May", Miss, but what a brilliant use of the rhymes "shines" and "declines" and "dimm'd" and "untrimm'd" and "ow'st" and "grow'st". We could spend ages discussing them, I expect, couldn't we, Miss?'

Kaye tailed off and subsided back into her chair, fearful that perhaps she had gone too far. She could not bear the others laughing at her. She could not explain, even to herself, what had made her want to speak out. Rachel gave her a little clap.

'I enjoyed that, Kaye. I don't think anyone could have put it better.' Kaye's day was made. Though she did not know it then, her whole attitude to academic learning changed with that lesson. She blossomed.

'Well, has anyone got more to add after that?' asked Rachel.

Silence. Then Siggy put his hand up, while still staring at the page in front of him. 'Kaye was good Miss, but I think she has missed something. I think you too have missed something if I may be so bold.'

'You may, Siggy, but make it quick. The bell will be going soon.'

'You say, or have perhaps implied, Miss, that Shakespeare is just trying to make the bloke feel good, because his handsomeness will live on forever, right?'

'Ye-e-e-s,' said Rachel cautiously. She had met this enigmatic side of Siggy before. 'Go on.'

'You know, that isn't the real point?'

'OK. So what is it?'

'Well, Miss, the crunch comes in the last two lines – the rhyming couplet:

So long as men do breathe, or eye can see,
So long lives this and this gives life to thee.

You see, Miss, what Faroukh said made me think. It's his, Shakespeare's, poem that will live on! It is "this" that will "give life" to his boss. I don't think he cares a fig about the everlasting beauty of the man, so long as his poetry lives on. The man will be nothing if it was not for this poem! That's what he wants to leave us with. What an ending! Cool, eh? Brilliant!'

Rachel stared at him. Once again Siggy, despite all his irritating habits, had hit the nail on the head. She could not help feeling proud of him.

'Well said, Siggy. Really good, close reading of the text. And that goes for all of you.'

And then the bell went as it often did in the middle of an interesting discussion and never did when the lesson was dragging, Rachel thought.

'That's a pity, Miss. We had just got going.' Cynthia was looking radiant.

'Don't worry, Cynthia, we'll be back to the sonnets, I am sure. And wait till we get on to John Donne.'

Lower Sixth English melted into the corridor crowd. Rachel started to gather her books and was suddenly aware that Keith was waiting by the side, last to leave.

'Sorry to bother you, Miss, but I just wanted to say that I thoroughly enjoyed that lesson.'

'Didn't you find it a bit chaotic, Keith?'

'Oh, I don't worry about that. If you're exploring the unknown you are bound to go down blind alleys, go up snakes and down ladders. We were all trying to tease out the meaning and I noticed that you did not try to dictate to us. You were really good – a referee rather than a player. Hope you don't mind me telling you that.'

If she did not know that she would be sacked for doing so she would have hugged Keith at that moment. 'Thank you so much, Keith. It is always good to get feedback. I appreciate it.'

'You're welcome, Miss. Oh, and I have penned a sonnet of my own to mark the occasion.'

'What! During the lesson?'

'No problem, Miss. I seem to be able to knock off lyrics at a moment's notice – not very good ones, but it amuses me. When I pen lyrics for my group I often go over the top with my tongue-in-the-cheek sentimentality. So it makes a change to have to keep to a strict metre and rhyme scheme. I'll leave it with you.'

He plonked his sheet on her table.

'Aren't you going to read it to me?' Rachel pushed it back at him.

'No, Miss.' Keith backed off. 'That would be much too embarrassing. I don't mind if there is a class there, but not on my own!' Keith touched his forehead in salute and made for the door.

'At least let me copy it for you.'

'Definitely not, Miss,' Keith replied over his shoulder. 'Like Ariel, it's gone now and so have I.'

Rachel contemplated his departing back and picked up the scribbled text.

The Lower Sixth were puzzled by Shakespeare,
Sonnet eighteen to be pernickety precise.
 Who 'thou' is in the poem was not clear;
To know for sure would be quite nice.
 Some plumped for the shadowy Dark Lady;

Some insisted it was an even darker man.
The Bard's motif for penning it was shady;
Was poesying for patronage his plan?
By guile their furrowed brows you diverted;
You squeezed their understanding over time.
It struck them how meaning is converted
By imagery, by rhythm, and by rhyme.
So, to grip young readers, setting minds on fire,
Know, problems dismay, challenges inspire.

It might not be Shakespeare but it is Shakespearean, she thought. 'How does he do it in the middle of a lesson?' She shook her head and leaned back in her chair, putting her hands behind her head. She sat contemplating for a moment, and then addressed the empty room. 'See that, you four walls! A good lesson was that. I've not a care in the world.'

'Well you should have,' said a voice from the doorway.

Rachel spun round in her chair. It was the Vice-Principal, Fred.

'What's the matter, Fred?'

'You should be on break duty, Rachel, not talking to the blackboard! The Principal is doing it at the moment, and he was second reserve.'

'So who was first?'

Fred smiled. 'It was me, but I had to find you, didn't I? He told me to hurry up about it!'

Rachel sprang up. 'Oh dear, Fred. That's the trouble with teaching. Somebody always wants you to be doing something else. Always something more important. I'll be out. straightaway!'

'Don't rush! It will do the Principal no harm to speak to a few kids on the playground for a few minutes. I'll tell him you were sorting out a serious student problem. You can explain what it was to him at your leisure, when you've decided what it was, of course! Necessity is the mother of invention. A very useful proverb, don't you think?'

'Thanks, Fred. Actually, nothing can dampen the joy of my last lesson. One of those occasions when you know deep down that you have made a difference.'

'I won't enquire now what went on. But you do intrigue me, so perhaps you will enlighten me later, eh?'

'Of course. But I will tell you this: problems dismay; challenges inspire.'

'That's neat. Who said it?'

'A philosopher, Fred – currently my very favourite philosopher!'

Howl, Howl, Howl

Know-all adults continue to be fascinated by one of the areas in which schoolboys, and indeed schoolgirls, are guaranteed to excel – the howler. The gems that follow are all answers to questions in 16+ modern language examinations, proving that all the developments and advances in teaching and learning have failed to curb the adolescent enthusiasm for extreme guesswork when it comes to understanding foreigners.

What is the 'entente cordiale'?
A soft drink made by the British and French.

What is a 'coup de grace'?
What a lawnmower does.

Why is the Eiffel Tower so called?
Because of its height. If you climb to the top you get a good eyeful of Paris.

Why is the Bastille famous?
It is the prison in Paris where the French started to be revolting.

What make Avignon famous?
It has a dangerous bridge and if you dance on it you might fall in the river.

For what is the island of Jersey renowned?
Potatoes and pullovers.

Name any three Impressionist painters.
Manet, Monet and Minet.

What was the importance of Bletchley Park?
This was where some very clever people translated the German highway code so that British pilots could make their way to the bombing sites.

What were Panzers?
Special German troops named after a well-known garden flower.

What in Spain is the flamenco?
It is a tall, graceful bird that likes to dance on one leg.

What was the Renaissance?
It means rebirth and it happened in Italy when Jesus was born again.

What was the Cubist movement?
Square dancing.

What is Europe's highest mountain?
Mont Plonk.

What is sauerkraut?
It is like bleach and Germans put it on their potatoes.

Name two German foods named after towns or cities?
Hamburger and Mainz baked beans.

Who is a 'burgermeister' in Germany?
An expert in making a Big Mac.

What is schnapps?
A German card game.

You just have to end with that one!

Taking the Strain

Newly qualified teachers in the first few weeks of their first ever job can be as stressed out as any other new employee. Marcus Brampton remembered this phase well. And told his old friends all about it at their reunion in The Babbling Brook.

My first month teaching in a south London secondary school went by in a whirl of unaccustomed activity – teaching thirty out of thirty-five lessons per week, learning the names of the three hundred pupils I was teaching, as well as getting to know my colleagues and understand the school's rituals and routines, preparing lessons and marking piles of books each night and weekend, taking rugby practice after school on Tuesdays and Thursdays, running the chess club on Wednesday, and then refereeing the Under-14 inter-school rugby matches on Saturday afternoon. I can honestly say that for the first month of my professional career I did not know whether I was coming or going. Nothing gets up a teacher's nose more than hearing other workers sniff disparagingly about teachers only being part-time 9 till 4 workers. If only.

Anyway, on the third Saturday of my first term I had just settled down to an evening of marking another pile of essays, having, of course, returned in a high state of excitement barely thirty minutes previously from the afternoon's Under-14 rugger match against local rivals St Swithun's, when I suddenly felt myself going hot and cold. I shot up bolt upright. There was something I had forgotten! I could not immediately think what it was. Then it dawned on me. It was now 6.45pm and at 7.30pm I was due to be at my Headmaster's and his wife's welcoming dinner for new staff at their home, which was at least half an hour's journey across the city. How could I be so stupid? Well, one reason was that I did not at that time have the benefit of a highly efficient diarist wife. I also consoled myself that it was, after all, school affairs that had absorbed my time and thoughts. Surely that would count in my favour? Nevertheless, I had to get there double quick, excuse or no excuse. First impressions are everything. It was in my own interests to show how on the ball I was.

I bounced into my charcoal-grey suit (my only suit), my old school tie (my only tie), and my brown suede shoes (my only shoes at the time). I was out of my flat and on my way within ten minutes.

Thus it was that I was knocking on the Head's front door barely fifteen minutes late. I had run to the underground, leapt down the down escalator two at a time, and up the up escalator two at a time, then run from the station and crossed the road, just on the yellow light. Thus, arriving at the Head's door I was a trifle out of breath, but, after composing my somewhat agitated features and running my fingers through my hair, I sized up the door.

The house was in darkness. No matter. Time was of the essence. I searched for the doorbell, found it, and gave a long imperious ring. Nothing happened at first. Still darkness. And then – blessed relief – the front porch light came on. The front door opened. There stood my Headteacher – the Head, the Beak, the Boss – in a black T shirt with a white logo that read, I noted, 'NO NEARER TO GOD THAN ME'. I took in the baggy brown trousers as well as the old carpet slippers and the Sherlock Holmes-type pipe hanging from his lips, which he removed as he peered at me. I looked him up and down and then stared him straight in the eyes; he stared back at me. Neither of us spoke. Then he nonchalantly crossed one leg over the other and leant on the door jamb, waving the pipe at me.

'Yes, Marcus, and what can I do for you at this hour on a Saturday?'

I knew then for certain what I had half worked out already.

'O Lor', Headmaster. It seems as though I've come on the wrong evening. It's next Saturday, isn't it?'

He did not reply immediately.

'No, Marcus,' said The Almighty slowly, 'it was last Saturday. And you were there.'

PERIOD TWO: WHAT HEADTEACHERS ACTUALLY DO

DANGER: Government Health WARNING:
TEACHING CAN SERIOUSLY DAMAGE YOUR HEALTH

Management by Ad-Hocery

During a lull in the conversation in The Babbling Brook, Marcus suddenly blurted out, 'You know what, the question that annoyed me most as a Headteacher was: "What do headteachers actually do?", always asked in a voice that suggested we did very little!' He did not wait for an answer. 'I'll tell you why it annoyed me – because it's not fair! Does anyone ask what a doctor actually does, or a lawyer, or a Member of Parliament, or a teacher? Well, actually, I expect they do. But that doesn't annoy me. Asking what a Head does is really annoying, because Heads themselves don't know actually!' Marcus quickly warmed to his theme.

When he was five years old, one of my sons was asked on a campsite in Italy what his father did. He thought for a while and then told the mother in the adjacent caravan, 'Well, he plays Santa Claus at Christmas in a red dressing gown.' True, but not wholly representative of my life's work. However, if that did not make me consider my vocation, then I really had to when one of the thirteen-year-old students at my school was asked by an Ofsted inspector what he thought the Head's job was. (I have no idea why he asked this but I have no idea what many questions about my role by inspectors, advisers, politicians, not to mention my own colleagues, were getting at!) Anyway, my lovely student answered, 'All I know is, he stands on the stage in the morning, says prayers and reads out the notices.' It is always a 'learning experience' to be told what others think you do. It is rarely comfortable.

The question therefore remains: 'What do Headteachers actually do?' After forty years in schools, I confess I was still searching for an answer when I retired.

It is easy enough to find out what they are supposed to do, what the nation expects of them. It is set out in the annual

'School teachers' pay and conditions document and guidance on schoolteachers' pay and conditions' issued by the government. Headteachers have a duty to provide overall strategic leadership and, with others, 'lead, develop and support the strategic direction, vision, values and priorities of the school.' The document goes on to explain these onerous duties in some detail.

When the first of these annual documents came out in the 1980s, my local authority produced its own portentous 'Framework: Headteachers, Managerial Tasks, and Competences – five pages of managerial tasks and competences (Problem Analysis, Adaptability, Organisation and Motivation, and so on). All very worthy, but I gather from today's Headteachers and Academy Principals that, as ever, the theory of 'a day in the life of a Headteacher' is somewhat different from the hurly burly of the ordinary school day. The Headteacher's legal responsibilities are generally carried out in an array of meetings, confrontations, writings, telephone calls, instant decision making, and seat-of-the-pants management. That is how things get done and how duties are actually discharged.

School management (I don't know about any other kind) is the technique of coping ad hoc with any circumstance that turns up, expected or unexpected. Ancient Roman leaders were very good exponents of 'ad hoc-ery' because they had plenty of experience of dealing with things on the spot, taking with them only the sketchiest of orders from Rome as they set off to all corners of the vast Roman Empire.

Management by ad hoc-ery is also a way of life for Heads. It can be measured ad hoc-ery, inspired ad hoc-ery, and at times charismatic ad hoc-ery; all of them can have one's colleagues gasping in awe and astonishment, or head-shaking in disbelief. That is how it is! And over the years school management has largely been carried out with the minimum of training. One became a Head because one had been a good teacher, even a Head of Department, or had served a sort of apprenticeship as a Deputy Head. Not until close to the end of the twentieth century was a National Professional Qualification for Headship (NPQH) instituted – and it was not, and is not, a compulsory certificate for headship. An independent National College for Teaching and Leadership was also inaugurated but was soon replaced by a Department for Education and Teaching Regulation Agency.

So, headteachers are better trained and better informed, but schools haven't changed! They still contain the same large tranches of humanity, the same intricate relationships, the same hopes, fears and challenges. And managing those is what headteachers do.

Moving On

In order to carry out the role of a Headteacher you first of all have to get a headship. In 'the old days' route one was via an advert in the Times Educational Supplement, *an application, references and interview; there were no such things as modern psychometric tests, person descriptions, two-day intensive on-the-job surveys, in-tray exercises and much else.*

After five years as a Deputy Head, Marcus Brampton had made his mind up. Now was decision-time; he either had to resign himself to remaining as a Deputy in his comfortable suburban grammar school for his next and final twenty years in the profession or take the plunge into headship. His decision was … to make a decision. He had done it before, and it had come to nothing. 'Real' life and the daily round kept him well away from any more such weighty concerns.

But this time his dithering was curtailed by a brief call at mid-morning break from his Head's secretary, asking him to take on the Head's lunchtime role of stalking the school premises – doing the Head's once-a-week duty. And why? Because the Head, had an urgent appointment.

'As usual!' said Marcus through gritted teeth. He knew full well that 'urgent appointment' was a code for a Rotary lunch. This solitary act convinced Marcus that it was time to be the giver of bad news instead of constantly being the receiver of it. Now was the was time to put his foot in the water in a time-honoured fashion by researching vacancies in the *Times Educational Supplement,* to suss out what sort of posts were on the market. So off he marched to the staffroom to peruse the job market.

There were hundreds of them. It was the time when the post-war baby boom had reached secondary school level, when new comprehensive schools were springing up everywhere, when there were not enough senior staff to fill the headship posts.

There were vacancies in independent schools, state schools, city schools, town schools, suburban schools, rural all-through schools and international schools, in the UK and abroad. The choice was perplexing. He mused over the advice he had received from friends who had moved into headship. 'Go for a school similar to the ones you've served in. That's the way to keep your sanity.' Sound advice perhaps, but unrealistic. The grammar schools he had served in, and the secondary modern schools that accompanied them, were on their way out. A plethora of 'comps' were on their way.

Marcus decided that the sensible approach was to send for the details of every single one of the posts being advertised.

And onto the doormat fell envelope after envelope of lengthy prose and bulky 'additional material'. As he ripped open each envelope, he became aware of an awful symmetry. Every single Local Education Authority, every Trust, every governing body, was looking for 'A person of exceptional ability; proven success at previous schools; outstanding leadership qualities; a person who can demonstrate an exemplary contribution to the school and wider community.'

'Wow!' thought Marcus in astonishment. 'Where are all these paragons? I can't say I have met many with that load of qualities. What about the ordinary bloke like me? Done a good job in the classroom, knows the ropes in the school corridors, and can smell a charlatan at twenty paces? Is there no place for the likes of me?'

He shared his depression with his wife. 'Don't be silly.' said Ros. 'It's just unthinking bureaucrats following the trend. They've seen what others have been saying and haven't bothered to actually think. If you are serious about getting a headship then just apply for the whole lot! That way you will find out which kind of employer likes what you say. Just set out your stall and go with it!'

You couldn't argue with that and so he applied for the first forty posts. And very shortly the first twenty brown envelopes flooded his hallway. He picked up what was the thinnest envelope of the lot up to that point, a brown envelope, with a single piece of folded A4 paper, marked 'from the Inner London Education Authority' - ILEA no less. It was the biggest education authority in Europe with hundreds of schools and dozens of separate divisions, revered by many for its investment in the arts, sport and minority groups and reviled by many for its waste of money on the arts, sport and minority groups. It was ripe for the chop by Mrs Thatcher, and eventually got it. But for the moment ILEA offered a safe haven.

Marcus ripped the envelope open and read on. His eyes widened as he read and his mouth gaped. Now here was something different! The single sheet had either been written by a divisional education officer near to retirement with a sudden urge for honesty, or perhaps an officer demonstrating the effects of being overworked and constantly overlooked. Marcus read it out to Ros.

HEADTEACHER VACANCY IN INNER LONDON

A Headteacher is sought for this all boys 11–16 comprehensive school of 1,500 boys close to the River Thames.

The school is a senior boys comprehensive school in the Docklands area of Inner London.

The school is housed in two buildings about a mile apart. The first three years occupy the Waterloo Road premises near the underground station. The older boys use the Marigold Lane building overlooking the docks. This building belies its outward appearance by being quite well equipped for some of its purposes.

Staff teach in both buildings. The Head has an office in both and receives a car allowance. Two bicycles are available at no charge for staff use.

The Local Authority expects to be spending a substantial, but as yet unknown, amount on modernising the buildings, eventually. Meanwhile, the Education Committee has agreed to the provision of a third bicycle from next academic year.

Most of the boys come from the largely working-class area around the docks, where parental expectations and pupil achievement have been traditionally low. On the other hand, there is a strong work ethic (paid work, that is) which often conflicts with the legal requirement to attend school. The school has always recognised this and has developed a wide-ranging work experience programme which, perhaps uniquely, runs throughout the year. It is strongly supported and welcomed by the staff.

It would be true to say that most of the pupils in this ten-form entry school are in the lower ability range, but the school does enjoy a local reputation for sound work in metal and wood.

The school believes in strong self-discipline and is working hard to learn how to do this. Some headway is being made with the staff, but more needs to be done with the pupils. Therefore, the current Head has relied on traditional discipline techniques – where possible. Detention has been found not to succeed as often as one may wish, owing to the fact that most pupils in the last two years are usually excused from detention for after-school employment reasons. Fixed term and indefinite exclusion by the school is patchy as many of the pupils have excluded themselves. However, exclusion remains a favoured technique for ensuring the desired environment for meaningful learning … by those who remain.

Corporal punishment is reserved for petty crimes such as theft and extortion, which are notably on the decrease at the moment since the long-term offenders have now been excluded.

There are good entries for the Certificate of Secondary Education (CSE) and the best candidates manage annually to get graded at some level or other. There has been a recent upturn in school-based and school-marked Mode 3 course-based CSE examinations in Parentcraft Studies, Navigation Studies, Sewage Studies, and Crime Prevention Studies. There is a gratifying take-up in all of them. Good results are anticipated in the future. But the courses tend to come and go, along with the staff.

The school takes pride in having won the borough crime prevention quiz for the past five years. The pupils' detailed knowledge and expertise have astounded the organisers.

During recent years the school has suffered from the difficulties arising from a low-ability intake, constant changes in staff and the pressures resulting from widespread and prolonged staff absence through ill-health. The fact that some progress has been made is due to the vigorous efforts of the present Headteacher and a small nucleus of loyal devoted staff.

The new head will need to be a man of courage, tenacity, resilience, determination, patience, stamina and firm discipline if he is to get the staff to work as a team – or in some cases, to work at all.

He will have the task of carrying men, and, in the case of the school secretary, woman, who have served faithfully but who are now limited by physical and mental debility, through no fault of their own.

The vacancy occurs because of the early retirement of the present Head who has served the school to the best of his ability.

'Goodness me!' Marcus murmured to himself. He did not apply for the post. A headship would have to wait another day.

Getting Ahead

Having applied for all the headship vacancies in the Friday *Times Educational Supplement* – except for the enigmatic plea for candidates by the Inner London Education Authority – Marcus Brampton was a bit more reticent to apply to any in the following Friday's batch. But then he noticed a short advertisement that offered a stark contrast to the London docklands: a call from a county shire he had never visited – except at speed down the M1. He read it carefully.

VACANCY FOR THE HEADSHIP OF A NEW COMPREHENSIVE SCHOOL

The County Council is looking for a Headteacher at a new co-educational comprehensive school currently being constructed on the edge of Market Upabit. It will serve a rural catchment area of some 400 square kilometres, bounded by Much Knowing in the north,

Lower Sodbury in the south, Stilby in the west and the edge of Fenborough City in the east.

It will be served by twelve village primary schools.

Further details from the County Education Offices.

Marcus considered that even though he had never taught in a comprehensive school, nor taught girls, nor taught outside a city, there was no harm in requesting 'further details'. So he did, and a week later received a very thin envelope containing one piece of A4 paper, with writing only on one side. It said:

VACANCY FOR THE HEADSHIP OF A NEW COMPREHENSIVE SCHOOL

The County Council is looking for a Headteacher at a new co-educational comprehensive school currently being constructed on the edge of Market Upabit. It will serve a rural catchment area of some 400 square kilometres, bounded by Much Knowing in the north, Lower Sodbury in the south, Stilby in the west and the edge of Fenborough City in the east.

It will be served by twelve village primary schools.

Application by letter (no forms) to the County Education Officer, marked Market Upabit Headship Application.

That was it! Exactly the same details!

A school and leadership post defined only by geography! Certainly worth a punt, thought Marcus. If nothing else, it would indicate whether his qualifications and experience would get him as far as an interview. But should he tell Ros, his wife, what he was doing? Yes, of course he must. Even though he knew that she would sigh once again, sigh and mutter 'vaulting ambition'. So, apply he did.

Two weeks later, after a series of rejections by previous targets, another thin envelope dropped on the mat: an invitation to attend an interview at 2.00pm in three days' time in the town council offices. No prior view of the new buildings, no preliminary briefing by an education officer; in fact nothing more at all. It seemed to Marcus for all the world like a stitch-up, with someone already groomed for the job. 'A rum one, certainly,' agreed Ros, 'but go for it. Any interview has got to be good experience.'

On the appointed day at 2.00pm in the Market Upabit Council offices, Marcus's suspicions were confirmed. Six candidates were herded into what was no more than a windowless walk-in cupboard and, taking charge, regaling the group with information about the new school and his part in an advisory capacity was the local secondary school head, one of the candidates. There was no sign of an education official, no pack of details about the new school, no site plan, not even a welcoming cuppa. It had all the hallmarks of the opening chapter of a Len Deighton spy novel. Marcus described later to his wife what transpired.

*****

As I sat there, gasping for a beverage, and someone to shut off the local man's constant chatter, I gradually began to warm to the idea of a new school in a new and wholly untried system, being defined so far in purely geographical terms. It might just be that the new Head would be left to get on with the job and would be judged by the outcome. I decided there and then that I was going to make a determined shot at getting the job. I would pull no punches; I would set out my stall in all the well-tempered hyperbole I could muster.

It was no good trying to disguise the fact that I had never lived in the countryside, taught girls, taught in a secondary modern school, or taught the CSE examination. But I reckoned I knew how to teach, how to help others to teach, how to support colleagues, how to inspire youngsters and how to build up a good reputation – oh, and how to construct a decent timetable. I'll give them two barrels of things to think about. That'll make them take notice, I thought.

But it didn't turn out like that at all, and this plan of attack had to be radically altered on the hoof, as soon as the first shot was fired. Like Trafalgar, Waterloo, the Somme and the Normandy landings, so now Market Upabit.

As the local man droned on, I surveyed the other four opponents. We were all men – two current Heads, a Deputy Head from inside the county, and three of us current Heads of Departments in selective schools. Only the local man knew anything more about the school than I did, so everything to play for. All we knew about the forthcoming interview was what we learned from a brief visit from the clerk, who popped into our dungeon, delivered his message and slid out again. We would each have no more than 20 minutes of interview; each panellist could ask one question and we would be given the chance to ask questions at the end – so long as they did not exceed a further ten minutes.

We had all forgotten to ask how many panellists there were, and those who had been interviewed were housed in a different cupboard – well away from those of us yet to be 'done'. So, when my turn came after a couple of hours of tea-less waiting (the fourth interviewee) I found myself seated on a chair placed along the fourth side of a hollow square. I looked around. Before me was spread an assortment of county councillors, interim governors, a senior education officer and a clerk – about fourteen in all, the most striking of all being a small, energetic lady wearing an army greatcoat and a very black eye-patch, who turned out to be one of the local gentry and designated Vice Chair of the new school's governing body.

In the centre was the Chair, the Leader of the County Council, Doris Cowan CBE – a femme formidable. She introduced her legionnaires one by one, but I couldn't take in any names or their qualifications for being there. I simply nodded at each one with what I hoped was a knowing look of someone with a total grip on the situation, which was not how I actually felt.

And so it came to pass. Each panellist did indeed ask one question, in varying degrees of innocuousness and irrelevance. I could see my plan to dazzle them with pedagogic brilliance was fast disappearing. The senior education officer was not

invited to contribute so there was no-one to ask a searching educational or management question (ie the ones I had banked on), and none of the others had ever been employed in a school, not that that deterred them. They all knew about schools, of course – after all they had all been to at least one as children!

'Will you cane girls for breaking rules, eh?' asked a red-faced farmer, seeming to relish his question and the vision it conjured up. When I curtly answered that I could foresee no possible occasion on which that kind of punishment would be appropriate, he leaned forward and quickly got in with a supplementary.

'I suppose that means you're one of those who object to thrashing boys who don't do as they are told, eh?'

He got no further. Doris the Chair had spotted the farmer's own transgression. 'Sorry Councillor Jerk. Only one question.'

'Aren't you going to cane Councillor Jerk for breaking the rules, Chair?' enquired a young, bearded man in a check shirt with a smile.

I placed him as a representative from the nearby steel town. The Chair had some difficulty in keeping a straight face.

'Please do not waste time Councillor Allshaw. Next question.' She turned to a pale-faced young man in an ill-fitting grey suit. 'Your turn Mr Skillithorn.' Skillithorn seemed surprised that questions had got to him so quickly.

'Er, er, won't you find it difficult to get to school on time, er, living, I note, about 50 miles away?'

At this, Doris the Chair exploded and shouted, 'Don't be silly. He won't be commuting! Ask another one.' But the abashed Mr Skillithorn was too shaken. 'No more questions, Chair.'

A local Lord then asked about my National Service in the army, followed by a local businessman with a son at the nearby independent school who wondered how I would get anyone to teach Physics at a comprehensive school. And then, just as I was beginning to despair, a wise-looking man, who turned out to be the putative Chair of the governors of the new school, asked me to describe my role as the head of a large department in a large school. No problem with that. A piece of cake. That disposed of the right flank of panel members.

Doris turned to the panellists on her left now. The Honourable Jezebel Fortesque leaned forward and peered at me with her good eye. 'How will you set about breakin' in new teachers, eh?' I learned later that she spoke mainly in horsey language, but at that moment I really didn't know what on earth she was getting at. I decided she would not appreciate my asking her to explain, so I launched forth into an explanation of what I would expect of staff appointed to this 'prestigious' new school. It seemed to satisfy her. She nodded and leaned back.

The questions moved swiftly on. One councillor did have the temerity to enquire what I thought leadership consisted of. I never got the chance to answer because once again Doris the Chair took charge. 'We haven't got time for philosophical discussions about leadership, Councillor Johnson. It's this committee's job to determine which candidate has *demonstrated* leadership qualities, not what they think it is.'

That was a pity. I would have liked to have explained my notion of leadership and perhaps to have illustrated it by telling the story of Noah, who was both manager and leader. Noah, so the story goes, showed good management skills by getting all the animals onto the Ark in good order, and then demonstrated excellent leadership qualities in making sure that the elephants did not get to know what the rabbits were up to! The first was a simple but skilful bit of sorting and arranging, ie management, while the second required vision and powers of deception as well as planning, all of which are classic leadership qualities as set out in Machiavelli's perceptive, and scandalous, exploration of leadership, *Il Principe* (*The Prince*). I thought it was a rather good illustration.

'Goodness me,' cried my wife, 'Surely you didn't—?'

No – actually, I probably would not have told this tale! But in any case, that question had been swept aside, and so we moved on. I did contrive to expand on each question and to turn it to what I wanted to talk about. You would have been proud of me struggling gamely to set out my meagre stall in the most glowing way I could.

Anyway, by the time the last question got to tail-end Charlie over on my right, all his potential questions had been covered. He pushed his piece of paper to one side, looked at me quizzically and asked rather apologetically, 'Are you healthy?'

Before I had stopped gaping like an out-of-water fish the Honourable Jezebel lifted her eye patch and boomed, 'He looks healthy to me!'

There was nothing left to say. I did not feel like following this with pseudo-philosophical questions, so I simply thanked them for their courtesy and left. I did not feel I had done enough to get the job, but perhaps nothing to throw it away either. It is probably how all candidates feel at that point.

Eventually we all gathered in our new cell and sat somewhat silently till close on 6 o'clock, fortified – at last – by one cup of tea and one biscuit. Never had these humble items felt so welcome. Then the door to our cell opened and the clerk looked around dramatically – like a TV baking competition chairman announcing a winner.

'Mr. Brampton, please come with me.'

And so the young whippersnapper from outside the county had done it. I remember feeling some sympathy for the five others who had shared the condemned cell with me for four hours, especially the local Head, but it did not last long. There were other things on my mind.

'Well, Mr Brampton. The committee has decided to formally recommend you to the Education Authority for appointment as Head of the new Market Upabit school. Will you accept our offer?'

'Yes, ma'am, I will,' I replied, 'but where is it?'

'Where is it?' repeated an incredulous Doris. 'Here, in Market Upabit. Where do you think?'

I cleared my throat. This did not seem a very auspicious start. 'Yes, of course, ma'am. But I haven't seen the site and it would be a bit odd to accept a job at a place one had never seen, not even a plan of it, don't you think?'

'Right,' announced the eminently practical Chair. 'Go now with the education officer. This lot will stay here with me till you return and then we will sign and seal it.'

And so the education officer whisked me up to the new school site, allowed me a quick survey of the various holes and piles of bricks, and a plan of what it might eventually look like, and then shunted me back again. The committee was just downing a final glass of town council British sherry when we arrived.

'Well, does the size of the hole appeal to you, young man?' Councillor Doris enquired.

'It suits me very well,' I replied.

'Then it's yours.' And she thrust out a hand - the deal was made.

'Well I never.' was all Ros could say. 'I suppose it will mean more new curtains.'

Team Building

My first task when I took up the Headship at the new school in Market Upabit, said Marcus Brampton, was to hire a few others – everything in fact from Deputy Head to cleaners. The first tranche of two hundred transferee pupils was due in September. It was now April and anyone currently in a post at another school had until the end of May to resign. Mindful of the peremptory way I was recruited and selected I vowed that I would be more 'professional' than that. But what was being 'more professional'?

Well, I was told, there was a vogue in business and industry for problem-solving exercises, in-tray exercises, professional quizzes, pre-interview classroom observations, on top of the familiar application forms, accompanying letters, references and interviews, all the accepted managerial paraphernalia of the times. But time was a commodity I did not have.

I explained to my wife, Ros, that at this point the Chair of governors, Andy, a long-time councillor and chartered engineer, came to my aid.

'Okay, it's your call,' said Andy, 'but consider this. The governors appointed you after an application form, two references and a twenty-minute interview. The "twitching nose" and "the whiff of success" triumphed over mere logic – and you can't say we got it wrong, can you?'

Well, no, I couldn't! A good point.

And so application forms, references and interviews it had to be. But at least, I vowed, I would take all day over it, inviting interviewees to morning discussions and question and answer sessions, followed by afternoon interviews – with a proper lunch and access to oodles of tea. It was, after all the English countryside the school was serving – four hundred square kilometres of fields, trees and five-barred gates. Tea out of china cups and cakes on patterned side plates seemed the right thing to do.

It all appeared sober and straightforward.

And it was – for most of the time. Chair Andy and I, and eventually my new Deputy, Olivia, sailed through candidate after candidate, congratulating ourselves on the astuteness of the appointments.

Then came the day when Andy could not join us. 'Never mind,' he said, 'Vice Chair Jezebel needs the experience.' So the Honourable Jezebel Fortesque joined the team – and did so on many more occasions as the years rolled by and the school grew.

Madame Vice was indeed a local dignitary, very active, much respected. No-one could overlook her. She was immediately distinguishable by her habit of wearing an army greatcoat, which, she told me, she had purchased from the Army and Navy Stores, and a black beret reminiscent of the wartime French maquisards. She also sported a black eye-patch following a horse-riding accident in her youth. A large shepherd's crook completed the picture – an image Breughel (the Younger) would have been proud of. She was by now in her 70s but during the Second World War she had been a sprightly ambulance-driver, I understand. For all her eccentricity she was highly entertaining and shrewd. Her unconventional approach to interviewing – well, to all life actually – made selection days with her a joy, and sometimes a trial! You see, she had a habit of talking in a horsey language of her own devising – highly metaphorical, totally uncompromising and utterly engaging – if you were not on the end of it.

She was not averse to asking candidates how they would rein in unruly pupils with bridle and bit, or what would be the first thing they would do after two hours with a hot and sweaty stallion between their legs on a Friday afternoon. She was referring, of course, to the importance of looking after your horse first following a day at the hunt, but not every candidate cottoned on to that straightaway.

'Do you mean … a horse?' asked one History hopeful timorously.

'I do,' replied Jezebel sweetly. 'What else do you think it might be?'

I have no idea what the lass replied. But I do remember when Jezebel fixed a specialist A-Level teacher with a mono-eyed look, and enquired casually, 'I can see you are good at giving high fliers their head, but can you do the mucking out in the main school?'

'I will muck out wherever I find muck,' replied the candidate, and promptly got the job.

Jezebel was bringing the art of interviewing to a new level. But that was not all. At the decision stage she had a habit of confounding the panel with her singular summing up of a candidate. They were peculiar, dotty, but somehow extraordinarily perceptive, as can be seen from the following examples.

About a candidate for a Science post: 'She needs to be put between the shafts for a month or two'.

A diminutive Maths teacher 'would never survive a good whipping.'

She found a budding Languages teacher, 'Good fetlocks … but a bit large in the nose.'

Of another candidate she remarked: 'This one looks as though he has been put out to grass – or ought to be.'

'That one needs her withers wringing.' This sounded pretty decisive until I realised that I had no idea what 'withers wringing' was!

Then came the most memorable occasion of them all. The panel had before them a twenty-two-year-old male PE candidate from a top PE college. He had applied for a post open to newly qualified PE teachers. When it came to Jezebel's turn to ask a question, she pointed a pencil at the candidate. 'What do you know about Ignatius Loyola, eh?' (Readers may know, I expect, that Ignatius of Loyola was a saint who founded the Roman Catholic Society of Jesus, known as the Jesuits). This poor lad, who just wanted to teach PE, did not know whether Loyola played outside left for Real Madrid or cricket for the West Indies, or what! His mouth dropped open, and he looked round the panel appealing for help! It was Deputy Olivia who sprang in to reassure him.

'Don't worry, Mr Miles. There are always questions that are difficult. If you don't know the answer just say so.'

He was clearly grateful, and his mouth closed. When he had finally left the room, I asked Madam Vice why on earth she had asked that question.

'Well,' she said, 'it was obvious he knew all the answers to teaching questions. But you need to see a PE teacher's reaction under pressure. We can't have a PE teacher with broken wind.'

So that was that! We did not appoint him. If my memory serves me right, we chose the one with shiny flanks, a good-looking pastern, and attractive mane. And you won't be surprised, either, to hear that all Jezebel-inspired appointments turned out to be first-rate. Uncanny – against the odds!

Natural Selection

Teachers and school support staff can be just as keen about getting particular posts as any other profession. It can lead to intense pleas to be heard and bizarre claims to attention. It is not surprising that most Heads have files full of comic extremes. Marcus Brampton, Head of Market Upabit School, told his pals in The Babbling Brook that he had a box full of 'memorable' applications.

'The first memorable reference I received came from a Head colleague in Wales,' he said. 'Very well-known in headteacher circles for his erudition, pedagogy and terseness. I had met him at some conference or other and requested, I remember, a reference for a Head of Mathematics. His reply read simply:

Dear Marcus,
I have received your request for a reference for Mr X.
I could not let a friend down.

Yours ever.

I confess that my interest in the language of applications and references began there. But before the references come the applications. In the days when jobs were hard to come by, or in subjects where there were more candidates than posts, the language sometimes became strident, sometimes frantic. Applications from abroad often had an added quaint touch, which could sometimes be beguiling and sometimes perplexing.

You may wonder why I have not been in school since March last. This is because I was sat upon by an elephant on Clapham Common.

We actually interviewed and appointed this candidate. It turned out that the incident had happened during a stroll across the Common where a circus was setting up.

The next gets a grade A for effort. But it was unsuccessful.

> You will note that I have put down that I have a BA degree. Well, I did not actually get a degree, but I had a damn fine try.

What heartache, but what strength of character and determination lies behind this next one.

> On my teaching practice I have been mugged in the classroom, arm-locked in the corridor, and threatened with rape in the cloakroom. Could you tell me whether you tolerate this behaviour in your school.

Sadly, I cannot remember whether we interviewed her. But we should have done. And then a really desperate one.

> I have applied for your chemistry post. If you have no vacancies in chemistry, have you any in history? I am particularly well up in nineteenth-century Malayan social history.

And one from a man, who had a touching belief in his all-round ability, included this:

> I have qualifications in painting, pottery, fabrics and nuclear physics.

It wasn't clear from his application whether he majored in Art or Nuclear Physics. We asked for a bit more information. He replied that:

> My degree was actually in Land Economy but I was told there was little call for that in schools.

The next smacks of a smidgen of desperation.

> You will be pleased to know I am above average size.

And another one came from an ancient colleague who sent me his favourite. It was, he suggested, from an applicant clutching at straws. Needless to say, it came to me in the early 1970s, not long after the university campus demonstrations. Heady times.

> I have had some administrative experience that you might find useful. At university I have organised two demonstrations and one sit-in. They were all very successful.

While this next one, from my own file, is also digging deep into the depths of his experience and qualifications.

I am well known as a good disciplinarian. I have certificates in wrestling, karate … and kickboxing.

And in a similar vein:

I started my career in a secondary modern school where I quickly learned archery and .22 shooting.

The next one, in response to a colleague's advert for a PE post with a willingness to lead outdoor activities, also exudes confidence and self-belief.

I have walked extensively in the Peak District and hold a St John's First Aid certificate, which I can renew. I feel competent to lead your proposed expedition to the Himalayas.

And then there were two trying the smarmy approach.

I have taught part-time in two big London comprehensives and have now resigned from them and moved to your part of the world because I want to teach in your excellent institution which deserves world-wide recognition.

And:

I know there will be hundreds of applicants for this post. If I am successful, I can assure you of my complete loyalty and devotion.

Another Head offered me these two 'little gems'.

I wish to apply for the post of Head of English. I have an exemplary health record apart from a period of absence last January following a fatal accident!

And:

> I have to be perfectly honest at the beginning of this application and admit that I was dismissed from my last teaching posit ion because of having an affair with the Headmaster's wife!!

My colleague wondered whether his rejection of the application was premature as it clearly demonstrated entrepreneurial and debonair tendencies that he liked to think indicated leadership qualities.

And finally, a snippet from a letter from a candidate applying for a Deputy post kept in my folder.

> I consider myself to be a natural leader. I am not a snob, but I do find my colleagues inferior to me.

The aphoristic nature of letters of application stemmed, I think, from the small space allowed for candidates to say something about themselves, although some candidates inadvisedly took advantage of the 'extra sheets' to just about write themselves out of the job!

Bookworm

Schools everywhere employ a small army of support staff, including classroom support staff, office staff, premises management, and technical assistants. Schools have their own procedures for making support staff appointments, but they are likely to include letters of applications and some kind of testimonial.

'Another "memorable" application arrived on my desk one day,' said Marcus, 'for a post as part-time school librarian. It was not the usual sort – not at all ...'

Dear Sir (or Madam),

I am applying for the job of Library Assistant advertised recently in the local newspaper.

I am, sir or madam, a young-looking forty-year-old, single, presentable, and unmistakably male, but currently unemployed.

I have had considerable recent experience of working in libraries as I find them warmer to read in than my digs. I also had experience of working in a library while at school, partly because I was often sent to work in the library by my class teacher, and once, when I was caught reading a novel in a Maths lesson, I was made library monitor for a week. This will undoubtedly be an invaluable experience in outwitting any of your more devious pupils.

I am what some people call a bookworm. I have over a thousand books on my shelves – most of them my own. I am, therefore, extremely knowledgeable. I am also big enough to prevent any pupil or teacher taking a book out of the library, if they dared to try.

I would like this position as it would enable me, in the comfort of your library, to continue my study of the Bible (King James Version, Revised, New English and Douai). I am doing this with the local congregation of a small but joyful sect of Wonderful Worship Witnesses. By comparing what they teach me with the various Bible translations, I am convinced that they are correct in their understanding of the prophecies. I fully intend, Jehovah permitting (Psalm 83: v 18 – King James Version of course), to be confirmed into their faith. This will entail lots of study, which your job will not interfere with, in order to obey the instructions of Jesus in Matthew 28: vv 19–20. As a Headteacher, you will know that is part fulfilment of His Sermon on the Mount (Matthew 24, especially v 14), which should be obligatory for anyone wishing to become a disciple, or a library assistant. Therefore, I would be earning my keep as a Christian should, while carrying on with my studies – all in the sanctified calm of your library.

Incidentally, can you tell me if it is a warm library.

I am yours – Psalm 8: vv 2– 3: 'Let my prayer come before thee and incline thine ear to my prayer, for my soul is full of troubles and my life draweth nigh unto the grave.'

Mr B Braddock

'I could not ignore that final flourish', said Marcus, 'so I sent a request to his referee for a character reference and received the following reply.'

Reference

Dear Headmaster,

I am sure Mr Braddock is not suitable for this position. He is a mountain of a man, better suited to kick-starting Boeings at Heathrow than stamping books. He could do well as a sceneshifter or furniture remover. He would certainly be able to shift bookcases around a library, but not keep them properly filled, I expect – or at least not with the right books.

Why he cannot find employment is a mystery. Perhaps no-one wants anything shifted these days, or he applies for the wrong job.

He has some very dubious friends, but as you are not employing them I will say no more.

He would be a very good disciplinarian, I think. At least, none of your pupils will hang around long in the library while he is there. He will be excellent at stopping children getting near the books, if that is what you want.

I have looked carefully at the details of the post and consider that it is a position that would suit me very well. Could you send me an application form.

(signed)

Neither of them were interviewed.

My Role in the Cold War

Marcus was well into the second bottle of The Babbling Brook's Côtes de Nîmes rouge. It not only stimulated the memory: it increased the desire to relate what he found there. Having now got into a flow about what Headteachers actually do, Marcus decided it was time to tell his colleagues about the strangest role he ever had to discharge.

I, like many other Heads, did not know when I accepted a headship post in a rural school in the 1970s that one of our Cold War roles was to be a 'War Duties Officer'. It was all part of the national civil defence plan that has now given way to general emergency planning, largely to deal with terrorist activity and natural disasters. But at that time many schools were earmarked as emergency sanctuaries in the event of a nuclear attack from the east – the USSR, ie Russia, or even China. Anyway, some diabolical threat from the east.

I suppose the thinking was that schools could organise reception of refugees, stash away hundreds of beds and bedclothes, and look after emergency rations to feed the population (those that remained alive). It was largely a fallacy. Few schools did have such a capacity, but it well illustrated the same 'can do', and 'go to it' spirit that got us through the two World Wars in the twentieth century.

None of this had I appreciated, or even given a moment's thought to, during my teaching career up to then, not, indeed, until a letter fell onto my desk within a few weeks of taking up my post as the first Head of this new school. It came in the usual morning pile of letters. I still have the original letter in my file, but I edited it for an after-dinner entertainment at a Secondary Heads Association dinner some time later. Here is the letter and my (and my Chairman's) reply to the letter received way back in the 1970s: a wholly different era from now, with a wholly different challenge, but you had to laugh or you would have despaired!

To: The War Duties Officer

Dear Sir,

Routine Test of Carrier Line 076/139

The following should be borne in mind by all Receiver Point Operators.

1. Test your receiver once per week. If you find a fault try banging the handset; it usually does the trick. If it does not, inform your superior War Duties Officer.
2. Remember to switch the battery off after use, because you may find it difficult to obtain new batteries in the event of a nuclear emergency. In our experience British Telecom are usually out of stock. However, bear in mind that some local stores or cycle shops may stock similar ones.
3. Remember that a nuclear device may have gone off – which will cause you some extra problems. It may be necessary to shout into the mouthpiece to avoid distortion. You will know when to shout if the sender is not able to hear you.
4. Read carefully your 'Instruction card' before hostilities commence.
5. Remember that if an attack is imminent it is advisable to climb into the large brown paper bag which has been provided in your War Duties pack, remembering to take your receiver with you.

(Now, you may think I made this up! I did not. It really was Civil Defence advice that brown paper gave protection against radio-active radiation – if you survived the blast. I still possess a copy of the Ministry's advice. It does not say where you can get large brown paper bags from once you have used the one provided, but in the 1970s bags of sugar were packed in large brown paper sacks as were loose potatoes and for a long time we had one neatly folded brown paper bag in a desk drawer at home! I kid you not! Oh, and we never did find the one that was supposed to be in the 'pack provided'. Come to think of it…. we didn't find the 'pack' either.)

6. When returning the Test card please remember to put a stamp on the envelope. Otherwise the General Post Office has assured us that it will be returned to sender.

After discussing the instruction with my Chair of Governors I could not resist sending the following reply.

Dear Sir,

Re your Routine Test letter

Your instructions were both interesting and enlightening, but ultimately left a lot to be desired.
  Here on the front line in rural England the situation is not as simple as you make out.

7. We do not have a carrier line, nor receiver.
8. There is no War Duties Officer, or if there is, he/she is well camouflaged.
9. We do not possess any brown paper bags. (Our greengrocer tells me there is currently a dire national shortage of brown paper sacks and flatly refuses to co-operate.)

However, the good news is that the postmistress has promised to get on her bike to deliver any messages you send in an emergency. And I have also ascertained that the local constable will gladly offer help – provided he is on duty that day.

We hope that meets the requirements and your approval.

Yours sincerely,

M Brampton
Headteacher

PS Presumably the enemy will give us rural denizens some extra warning time in the light of our communication difficulties. Otherwise it would not be fair.

Not surprisingly I heard no more. But it obviously worked as the town was never attacked.

The Artful Dodges

Donny Dodge was not enamoured of school. In fact, he preferred to be anywhere else – and often was – but he was a wily entrepreneur, and sometimes business took precedence over school. He is the only student Marcus Brampton, Head of Market Upabit Academy had ever come across who has advertised his truancy in a newspaper!

Donny was son of the owner of the Market Upabit garage, grandiosely called Executive Motors Garage. He had been off school for nearly a week, claiming via several notes signed (allegedly) by his father, Donny Sr, that he had a heavy, very debilitating, throat infection. On the Thursday morning before school opened, Mr Brampton was idly flipping through the local newspaper, looking for a replacement for his old Volvo Estate, when he came across a small advert for a week-long, never-to-be-repeated 'Grand Sale' of 'exceptional re-tread tyres'.

That was unremarkable, but at the bottom his eye caught – in bold lettering – '**RING AT ANYTIME, DAY OR NIGHT, AND ASK FOR OUR EXECUTIVE, DONNY**'.

'Donny!' he shouted to himself. 'Donny Dodge! Year 10. Of course! It would be! Well, well, the little blighter. Day and night, eh?' I'll "executive" him, all right.' He checked that Donny was indeed absent from school and then rang Executive Motors.

A youngish voice attempting to be posh but with a marked local twang answered. 'Executive Motors. Sales Department. Sales Executive Donny speaking. What can I do for you?'

'Donny!' yelled Marcus down the phone. 'Mr Brampton here. Get back to—' He got no further. There was a loud fit of coughing at the other end and a croaky voice whispering, 'I have been really poorly, Mr Brampton, a chest infection—'

'I thought you'd told the school it was a throat infection,' said Marcus, breaking into Donny's flow.

'Err, yes, it was. But it's gone down to my chest now.' A further bout of wheezing followed.

'Well,' replied Marcus after a pause. 'That sounds very bad indeed. I'd better send the Attendance Officer along to assess the situation.'

Donny's reply came swiftly in a less throaty yell. 'No need for that, sir—' The fit of coughing began again. 'Funny things these chest colds, sir. They come and go quickly you know. I'm feeling a lot better already. Matter of fact, I was just thinking of ringing the school. I'm sure I can make it back tomorrow.'

'Tomorrow, Donny? How about *now*?' said Marcus slowly and deliberately.

A short pause, then 'Yes, Sir. I think you have caught me at a good moment. I will struggle back'.

'Do that, Donny. I know life can be a struggle, but it is usually worth the fight. Get here in the next hour and you'll find life going on much the same as you vaguely remember it. We will be very understanding – and fair.'

He did and they were.

But Marcus hadn't finished with the Dodges. Donny's sister Bonny was not much better than her brother at attending. She had a portfolio of excuse notes, some more plausible than others, but all duly signed by mother or father, and occasionally, Mr Brampton surmised, by brother Donny, too.

Among the gems were: 'Bonny cannot make school today because of a coleslaw which she cannot get rid of.' And: 'Bonny suffered a blow to her head when she cycled home after games and stopped at the pub … for a shandy. It was dark and she rode into the wrong drive. She banged her head on a tree we have not got.' Bonny, it seems, was the second most accident-prone pupil in the school, second only to her brother Donny.

Finally, after one too many absence excuse notes and thoroughly exasperated at having yet another absence reported to him, Marcus Brampton rang the Dodge home.

A female voice answered rather brightly.

'Hello.'

'Good morning,' said Marcus, conjuring up as much politeness as he could muster. 'Mr Brampton, Market Upabit Academy here. I'm enquiring after Bonny. She seems to have had a lot of time off school.'

The voice at the other end changed to a deeper, gruffer tone, a touch more adult but not quite getting there. 'Oh yes. I'm afraid she has been very ill, you know. Very poorly indeed. We told the school some days ago, Mr Brampton. I told Mrs Thingy that Bonny was in bed with the doctor and, I'm afraid, it doesn't seem to be doing her any good….' (pause) '….Throat still very, very bad.'

'Oh really,' growled Mr B. Then, raising his voice a little, 'Who am I talking to?'

There was a quick response.

'Me mum.'

Taking Care

'Headmasters have powers at their disposal with which Prime Ministers have never yet been invested.' (Winston Churchill, My Life (1930)). But Churchill had reckoned without caretakers! Caretakers have the school keys, know how to turn off the boiler, and keep the premises litter-free. That is actually more power than any Head has dreamed of!

It is not often that a school caretaker gets a major billing in documentaries or novels about schools. But just as important as the teaching staff is the appointment of the school caretaker, aka the Premises Manager or the Site Manager or the Safety and Security Manager, multiple roles all wrapped in one person leading his/her dedicated team of knowledgeable, skilful colleague, often paid as skivvies. It is noticeable these days that many large schools have trained and experienced premises managers, but it was not always the case, as Marcus Brampton recounted.

Market Upabit's first caretaker was a 50-year-old ex-Chief Petty Officer from the Royal Navy. Ted had been caretaker for some years at a local primary school so he already knew some of the pitfalls of the job. He worked hard to keep our premises clean and well maintained. My senior colleagues and myself shared his drive for high standards, but his methods were often, shall we say, esoteric – eccentric, some might say. He had a naval man's penchant for 'good, ship-shape order' which sometimes expressed itself in extraordinary ways.His approach to maintaining order in the school car park and access roads was a case in point. His technique was to nail up on a BT telegraph pole at the edge of the car park a myriad of signs, all pointing towards oncoming drivers and pedestrians as they entered the premises through the front gates.

At the very top was a large 'NO ENTRY' sign. Quite what this imposing prohibition notice was designed to prohibit was not clear since the cars and pedestrians were already fifty metres onto the school site before being confronted by it, and there was no apparent 'ENTRY' beyond the telegraph pole to be barred from. But, since I had told him (perhaps in an excess of delegation fever) that he was 'in charge' of notices, I could hardly take down his very first one. Myself and my Deputy decided that no apparent harm could ensue, so we should just leave it. And leave it we did.

Within days a veritable cornucopia of messages joined the first one. Each one was painted in alternating red and black on a piece of white board and then affixed neatly under each other, starting with 'SPEED LIMIT 5 MPH ONLY'. This appeared on the Tuesday, with the remainder appearing each morning from Wednesday to Friday.

'ONE WAY ONLY'
'DRIVE WITH CARE'
'DO NOT WALK ON THE GRASS'
'WALK ON THE LEFT'
'VISITORS REPORT IMMEDIATELY TO RECEPTION'
'HAVE YOUR IDENTIFICATION READY'
'TRESPASSERS WILL BE PROSECUTED'
NO DOG WALKING ALLOWED'
'DELIVERIES AT THE REAR'

and finally,

'DANGER. BEWARE STUDENTS'!

Each of these was clear and informative but pinned one above the other on the telegraph pole at the side of the school car park constituted a bewildering experience for any visitor. After another week, and following growing staff and governor scepticism, I resolved to intervene. Ted's persuasive method

103

was, as you would expect from a Chief, direct, no-nonsense, incontrovertible.

'My job is to advise you on how to keep the premises safe,' he asserted. 'This is how you do it. Informing people coming onto the site what is expected of them will ensure that any claims of negligence will not succeed.' He went on to explain gently to a sceptic, me, that putting them all together in one place was quite clearly preferable to the alternative of having them dotted willy-nilly round the car park causing confusion. I gave in. Some arguments are better lost than won at a cost!

The signs stayed and did their job, until one day one of Her Majesty's Inspectors of Schools (HMIs) arrived at my door with tears welling in his eyes. I was not sure whether they were tears of hysterical laughter or despair.

'What on earth is the matter,' I said. He took a little time to compose himself before he replied.

'I was trying to read all those b****y notices. I had only got to the third – the one that says 'DRIVE WITH CARE' – when I ran into the telegraph pole!' He wiped away another tear. 'My new BMW's radiator has caved in.'

It took all his sense of fair play and my tortuous explanation – trying to remember what Ted had explained so ingenuously to me – to persuade him to go through his ritual survey of the English Department. I was never again able to look a BMW in the radiator without pangs of guilt.

And so the signs, and the pole, had to go. Ted was not happy, but he saw my point. But that was not the only one of Ted's 'little schemes'. He had loads more. The following tale will illustrate the clash of cultures: school and ship.

In the first month after our opening, Ted was infuriated by boys, and occasionally girls, removing toilet-door knobs, or fastening the toilet doors from the inside and then climbing out, so that no-one could get in, or loosening toilet seats (all of which, I might say, were ridiculously cheap and fragile, so that pupils using them slid off in mid-stream, as it were).

One day I caught Ted with his saw and screwdriver about to saw a metre off the top and bottom of all the toilet doors and partitions, leaving just a small central section to provide for modesty. Heads and legs would be clearly visible. I went pale with anxiety. What on earth was he playing at? His argument was that this is apparently what toilets were like aboard his Navy ships. It enabled petty officers to look down a line of toilets and ensure there was nothing untoward going on. 'That's why they are called "heads" on board ships,' he said authoritatively. 'You can see immediately if there is any hanky-panky.' (It is not true, by the way. Ships' toilets were called 'heads' because they were placed at the 'head' or bow of the ship.) But I did not care whether it was true or not. I could see large headlines in the local newspaper looming – not complimentary.

'No!' I cried. 'Don't do it! This isn't the Royal Navy, Ted, and we'll have parents round here complaining before the day is out!'

It was a close call!

The Burning Question

At the new Market Upabit Comprehensive School, there was continuous building for years, as the school grew. Phase 2 of the building programme was scheduled to be completed during the summer holidays at the end of the second year, when the first of the large comprehensive intakes would be arriving from the feeder schools. It was an important moment in the school's history. Governors, Head and staff had been planning the great advance for months.

Headteacher Marcus Brampton was all geared up to take over the new Science laboratories and Sports Hall on the last day of August. 'And we would have done,' said Marcus, 'but fate was against us.'

On the Thursday before the end of the holidays he went with his uncle to watch a Test Match at Lords. They arrived home after midnight and Marcus's head had hardly touched the pillow when the 'phone rang. It was the school caretaker, Ted, who lived in the bungalow on the school site.

There was no messing! 'Sorry to bother you, Headmaster, but can you see a red glow in the sky from your window?'

Marcus looked out of the window. Our house was barely 100 yards from the school. 'Yes I can.'

'Well, that's your school burning down!'

Whether there is any official guidance on the correct headteacherly response to such information is not known. What Marcus did was curse profusely, don some clothes over his pyjamas, fling on an anorak and race up to the school. 'I don't think my wife even woke up, I was off so fast. Certainly, neither my uncle or son did,' he said later to his Chair of governors. Marcus described what happened.

*****

I got to the scene double quick. The roof of the gym was well alight, and because it was a school just about every engine

106

in the county, the next county and the nearby city was already there.

The Chief Fire Officer in charge made himself known to me in the glare of the floodlights. He strode off through the lit area into the gloom and I hurried after him. I was determined to accompany him as he went round checking which engines were actually there.

'Where are you from?' he asked the first crew.

'Market Upabit Volunteers,' replied number one.

We hurried to number two.

'And you?' to the second.

'Much Knowing Volunteers.

'And where are you from?' to the third.

'Fenborough,' said a voice in the dark.

Then on to the fourth, who peered up from the end of a nozzle, which was firing machine-gun-like jets into the flames.

'Where are you from, mate?' said the Chief.

'Eh? Can't hear! What did you say?' yelled a yellow-clad voice.

The Chief cupped his hands and yelled back.

'Where do you come from?'

'Rawalpindi,' came the speedy answer.

'Bloomin' heck! You got here fast.'

The Chief was one of those who had an instant answer to anything. You must have met them! Maybe you are one.

You will be glad to know that the fire was soon under control. It turned out that a workman had been using a gas cylinder on the roof to heat the bitumen, and knocked off work with the nozzle still burning ever so slightly. After a few hours it burned a hole in the roof material and the whole lot caught fire.

It was November before the school opened its Sports Hall and laboratories, but it got a bit of extra history as well. And it has all come to light (as it were) via my scraps of notes.

*****

And so ended another piece of the ad hoc-ery which fills a Head's life.

107

Human Resources

Much of a Headteacher's time is spent dealing with, or avoiding, confrontations with such troublesome thieves of time as teachers, support staff, parents, governors, local authorities, inspectors, and, occasionally, pupils, and anyone else bent on disrupting the Head's peaceful daily round – advertently or inadvertently. Amidst the heartache and strife lies rich comedy as the parties strive to better the opponent – or at least come out equal. But management by email can be fraught with dangers. It is always better to sort out problems face to face, said Marcus, as Miss Edith Flutter, Head of St Agnes Girls Preparatory and Senior School, Much Knowing, learned when trying, by email, to help the new, bursar deflect a 'HR' problem.

MEMO

From: B Showall, Bursar
To: Miss Flutter, Headmistress
Subject: Personal relations between Matron and Caretaker

Headmistress,
I feel that the personal problems of Ms Debra Size, the matron, and Mr Hardman, the caretaker, which I made you aware of last week, can now only be solved by a strong union. In the mood they are in, it would be easy to arrange it, but there is a dilemma. The matron would like a professional association, while the caretaker prefers a manual union. Would you now like to have a hand in this somewhere? Personally, I think we should consider a pincer movement, me taking a lateral position while you make the quick, sharp thrust down the centre. That should take them both by surprise.
B Showall (Bursar)

MEMO

From: Miss Edith Flutter, Headmistress
To: Mr Bartholomew Showall, Bursar
Subject: Personal relations between Matron and Caretaker

Bartholomew,
I appreciate very much your suggestion that I might participate in this affair. I agree that I might have the necessary experience to interpose myself between matron and caretaker. I also agree that a direct open approach with no holds barred might be productive, but at this moment I am happy for you to carry on with your 'watch and listen' strategy and to encourage the forming of a productive union. Perhaps you could now summarise the various positions of the parties and advise me on what options are open to us.
(And, by the way, although my appellation is 'Headmistress' or 'Principal', I like to be addressed by my first name, Edith. I find it brings one so much closer to one's colleagues.)
Edith Flutter, Headmistress

MEMO

From: Bartholomew Showall, Bursar
To: Miss Edith Flutter (Edith), Headmistress
Subject: Personal relations between Matron and Caretaker

Dear Edith,
I apologise for getting your title wrong. I am learning the ropes and am fearful of getting too intimate with senior management at this point, although I applaud your policy of using first names, of course.

As I see it, the main problem consuming the matron and caretaker is one of possession. Possession is close to both their hearts.

The caretaker keeps his equipment exclusively for the use of the cleaning ladies, which, I am afraid, is infuriating matron. She has warned him and me that she is contemplating invading his private areas in order to access the equipment she desires. She says that she has a right to avail herself of the caretaker's apparatus, as this has been her custom with all his predecessors.

I observe that their efforts to get on top have exhausted them. It is time for one of them to give way. However, although I firmly believe that they have made their own bed and must now lie on it, I fear we must soon step in and prise them apart.

I suggest there are three classic positions we could adopt:

1. A one-to-one – without a union or association, you could take on the caretaker, leaving me to grapple with matron
2. The two of us – confronting the union, with possibly a neutral member hanging around for our mutual benefit.
3. A threesome – with you taking on both of them at the same time. I will hover in the background to step in if and when required.

But we must act quickly before their respective positions become evident to all. If we delay it might become impossible to hide the affair from unseemly public scrutiny. I would welcome your experienced advice.

Bart Showall, Bursar

MEMO

From: The Headmistress
To: Bursar
Subject: Personal relations between Matron and Caretaker

I have decided not to become entwined in this matron/caretaker affair at this stage. The issue of the school's exchange with a Paris lycée is now occupying my full attention, and my liaison with Le Proviseur Monsieur Alphonse Legrand is proving quite unexpectedly exciting, not to say exhausting.

I suggest you seek skilled professional advice as you suggested, before you get yourself into the sort of hole you cannot easily extricate yourself from.

Edith Flutter, Headmistress

The Issue of the Tissue

From the 1990s onwards, schools were given an increasing control over their finances, culminating in the introduction of self-managing state-funded academies, and finally 'Academies'. This was accompanied by enhanced roles for boards of governors, and especially chairs of school boards. A new breed of business-like chairs and school boards was anticipated in the Department for Education's Governance Handbook, and still is. But there was an oldy-worldy, Wooster-ish charm about twentieth-century governing bodies that inevitably clashed with the modern demands, as in the following exchange between Headmaster, Marcus Brampton, and his new chairman of the governing body.

MEMO

To the Chairman of the governing body, Colonel Wilfred Clutterbuck

Re: Your last memo concerning your 'Order of the Day', and your request for information about the 140 boxes of toilet rolls you have, in your own words, unrolled.

I understand that the governors' Health and Safety Sub-Committee discovered during their recent annual tour of the premises, 100 boxes of superior toilet paper in the boiler house and 40 more in my own personal toilet room. You ask for an explanation.

May I remark at the outset that I welcome wholeheartedly the governing body's resurgent interest in Health and Safety issues and the new policy of injecting a fresh rigour into the discharge of governors' duties following the devolved financial powers to schools. Of course, I support fully the policy of demanding the utmost care and attention by staff charged with accounting for the purchasing of goods.

I am in total agreement with your urgently expressed view at the last meeting with cleaning staff that in regard to stocking the toilets, we must start with a clean sheet and make a clean sweep from the bottom up. A timely and inspiring message. They could not fail to be uplifted by your call to bend their backs, grasp the matter in hand and strive with all their might to release our latent energies. No one could fail to be moved by your heartfelt plea.

You say in your recent memo that you are perplexed by the staff reaction to your 'Order of the Day'. I do not agree with you that there was any disrespect in the laughter that followed your address. Mr Snodgrass was quite put out when I told him that you thought he had muttered 'silly old basket,' when he had actually said, 'How silly that we had not thought of it.' However, he fully understands the difficulty of the acoustics in the new award-winning high ceiling atrium where we now have to meet on account of the noise of the air conditioning system in the windowless staffroom. We all appreciate your sympathy on the numerous occasions that I have drawn it to your attention. No doubt at some point I shall also be able to report some action.

As for the rest of the staff, may I reassure you that their recognition of your leadership has not diminished one jot since the meeting last year when you announced the criteria you were going to use in determining salary increases in the future. They may not have been familiar with the battlefield terminology, but they did understand what you meant by 'men (and I know you included women in your stirring words) performing gallantly under fire' and 'officers and gentlemen leading with the bayonet from the front'. It is just a tad difficult for them to translate this into teaching Year 7.

However, I grant that it was the tonic you predicted it would be. It certainly galvanised a previously docile and acquiescent staff. And, of course, it was not possible at the time to foresee that the school would be facing an Equal Opportunities Commission investigation into the school's gender discrimination. We do indeed live in an unprecedented age of liberal values, as you say, and I can fully appreciate that this can be disturbing to persons dedicated to upholding the 'old bulldog qualities', as you so colourfully put it.

I agree, of course, that the Equal Opportunities Commission is perhaps lacking in a robust understanding of traditional army jargon, but some of the words you conjured up were beyond my or my colleagues' immediate comprehension. Incidentally, what does 'the effing effer's effing-well effed it' mean in relation to the Commission's last decision in favour of the union? It has quite foxed both my colleagues and me. If suitable, we could set it as a parsing exercise for Year 8.

But to return to the toilet roll problem. You have, may I say, touched on a sensitive issue here.

You will be aware that the school is blessed by a number of elegant ladies, with delicate tastes. When you directed a change to hard toilet paper, similar to that provided for HM forces in the field, on the ground of economy, you will remember that we had a little difficulty with the staff.

I supported you in principle, but you will recall I doubted the wisdom of refusing to consult the unions which, as you know, resulted in the first referral to the Equal Opportunities Commission on the ground that ladies' toilet paper needs are well known to be more sensitive than those of men.

I do not in any way judge the previous approach to this touchy subject. But the fact remains that something had to be done, and I did it.

With your exhortation to school leaders 'to get their hands dirty,' and 'catch the enemy with their trousers down,' and 'never to pull the handle till the tank is full,' ringing in my ears, I have ordered the caretaker to collect all the staff toilet paper and to re-stock with perfumed lilac three-ply. In so doing I took full account of your drive for economy. I arranged for all the rolls to be sliced in half and issued an edict that staff toilet paper would be kept in my office, where individual staff could collect one sheet at a time.

This has not met with universal approval. Therefore, we may need to meet shortly to consider the consequences of a third referral to the EOC.

Marcus Brampton
Headmaster

115

The Persistent Parent

One of the many skills of Headteachers is knowing how and when to respond to parent concerns and complaints – particularly when they come thick and fast, and from just one source.

One of the parents Marcus Brampton had to deal with was a father of two splendidly normal children. His wife would not say boo to a goose, whilst he on the other hand was an inveterate complainer, and devoted letter-writer. It was not that he did not have legitimate points to make about the education of his and other children. It was the way he made them – again, and again and again.

Marcus now had a large file of letters the said parent had sent over the years. He treasured one in particular. This letter could reasonably serve as a kind of 'in-tray training exercise' for aspiring or new Heads. Budding Heads could be asked, 'How would you respond to this?'

Dear Headmaster,

I acknowledge receipt of your letter to parents of the 5th inst, though I cannot say that I thank you for it.
With reference to its contents, ie urging parents of Year 11 students to consider their children's school commitments when considering their part-time employment, your cool, legalistic approach to the important issue of child employment is not adequate. You are arguing from too narrow a base. Marx himself acknowledges that there must be a base on which to build. You are rather like the highway squad who patch up holes when it is the foundation of the highway that needs reinforcing, or like the parson who resorts to the Bible when his Sunday school class deserts.

The situation is exacerbated in a developing area like this, where the wealth of the indigenous people – even when equal to the newcomers – is not exploited to the same extent as the latter. This is, of course, obvious, but I think you need to be reminded of it, because it leads to the important question: What are *you* going to do about it, Headmaster?

While living in the oblivion of the northern uplands of your catchment area I have thought long and hard about this, and recently rang the Vice Chancellor of Leeds Metropolitan University to get his view. As we live a hundred miles from Leeds he was quite surprised – especially as he could not work out how I had got past his secretary in order to talk to him.

I spoke to him at length. For a while he seemed to find my arguments difficult to understand. He persisted in saying that he had not understood the question. However, when I continued to press him, he did admit that I might have a point, but could not accept me on a PhD course on the strength of one telephone call. I had thought it worth enquiring about the doctorate course when I became aware that the university obviously needed an injection of academic rigour. The Vice Chancellor had not, up to that point, appreciated the urgency. I was in the middle of convincing him when his secretary informed him of an impending meeting.

I have been unable to catch him in since then but have booked a call to his office next week when he will certainly be in, as the Prime Minister is visiting the university. I look forward to discussing his conversations with the PM after the event.

I am also taking the opportunity to tell you that after a number of postponements I have arranged a lunchtime meeting with your Head of Sixth Form concerning her organisation of the Sixth Form. Below are the references from which I plan to develop my argument, over the next few weeks.

Leighton, *Guidance and Counselling: A Beginners' Guide*
Hardy, *Revolution: a new approach*
Bristow, *A Society at Odds*
Bulkman, *Education without Schools*
Sperling, *Psychology made Simple*
Quoist, *Meet Christ and Live*

I assume you have read them. I would be interested to know whether you think that these will cover the subject adequately.

Incidentally my daughter came home today and told me your Head of Music had said her recorder was flat. As I have perfect pitch, I compared my C with the recorder's C and found it perfectly in tune 8 times out of 10. I presume it is your piano which needs attention.

I have also mentioned to you in the past that during her time at your school my daughter has developed a fixation about 'Health and Safety in the home'. I wonder if she has misunderstood her Home Economics teacher, as this distorted middle-class emphasis on washing and cleanliness is beginning to irritate me greatly.

I also consider a bottom E grade rating in French is not really encouraging when considered against the five major points in Catholic education emphasised by the Archbishop and endorsed by Rome. An E grade is the mark of shoddy secularism and against the strong principle of in loco parentis which is the bedrock of the pedagogic profession.

You will know from our previous exchanges (although I have not yet received replies to my letters of the 10th ult and 1st inst) that my ideas circulate in my mind and in the community until they reach an organic truth, in true Gestalt psychological fashion. This is happening right now.

My daughter was in a very agitated mood after I had talked to her yesterday. It is no wonder that she did not do her French homework last night, which is what I am writing to tell you.

Yours etc

Marcus confronted his Senior Management Team, who were united in baying for action when they read the letter, although less united about what the action should be.

'Look,' said Marcus, 'three things you might understand from the above letter. The first is that the writer was in the middle of the Open University Sociology course. The second is that there was not a cat in hell's chance of my winning any argument. And the third is that both I and the school would flourish rather better if a confrontation was avoided altogether.'

This brought protestations from senior colleagues.

'They were more attracted to Tudor jousts than me,' Marcus said later to wife Ros. 'I just ignored it and discretely recommended to the Head of Languages that the daughter should be given time at lunchtime to finish the homework and receive his undivided attention while doing it. Cowardly? Well, possibly. Pragmatic? Well, definitely!'

Nothing more was heard about this issue. Marcus finally navigated the parent's children out of the school and on to further education, where incidentally they had greater knowledge of Sociology and Psychology at that time than any other student had – and probably more than some of the lecturers!

Marcus summed it up thus: 'It also confirmed my colleagues' view that I was indeed more the Neville Chamberlain than the Winston Churchill when it came to considerations of war and conflict.'

The Unexpected Parent

Normally parents are impressive examples of motherly and fatherly care and thoughtfulness. They are also – in the main – appreciative of all that teachers are achieving and intending to achieve. But naturally their first thoughts are for their children's welfare and development. This can lead to occasional conflict which, one hopes, will be sorted out in a civilised and caring manner.

But there were other attitudes and approaches. Some parents are, shall we say, headstrong, and prone to defy the normal rules of civilised engagement. They simply do not believe that there can be any interpretation of the course of events other than their own. And that can lead to the well-known condition 'Headteacher Extreme Panic Mode' in response, as Marcus Brampton found out early in his headship career.

Bernard Riley, the son of a local builder, an Irishman, bunked off PE one day. He simply walked out of school and made it to the building site where his very tough and uncompromising dad was working. He told his pater that he had been subjected to the very worst, severe form of backside punishment (when such things were still legal) delivered by the PE master, Mr Wilkins. Without enquiring further Dad downed tools and roared into school on a very fast motorbike, leaving his son to find his own way home. Father eschewed the etiquette of calling in at Reception and was spotted by the alert receptionist, Angie, hotfooting it down towards the gym area.

Now, telephones in schools at that 'before-mobile-phone' time were in short supply. Only the School Office, the Head and occasionally the staffroom were eligible. But in Marcus's Market Upabit School, the Head of PE, Adrian Wilkins, had a phone simply because his office was in the Boys changing room and the school's female secretaries would be obliged to run the gauntlet of naked males to carry any of the myriad of calls that PE teachers receive, a prospect that horrified nearly all.

And so, on getting the news of Riley Senior's arrival, Marcus leaped into Plantagenet action, crying, 'Leave it to me!' He made a frantic call down to the PE department, confident that this decisive decision-making would save the day, only to find that Murphy's Law was in play – the phone line was engaged. The 'idiot', as Marcus unfairly branded his unknowing Head of PE, was at that moment talking to somebody else.

'Get off the b**** y line!' Marcus shouted vainly down the phone. The engaged ringtones were still mocking him the next time he tried.

'O Lord,' he cried to himself, 'there'll be blood everywhere!' Then he noticed Deputy Vera standing in his doorway.

'Mr Riley is trying to sort Adrian out. We have to stop him! What on earth was the man playing at, beating a boy when it is against the school rules – there'll have to be an inquiry!'

'Don't worry about that now,' cried Vera and she disappeared from sight.

'Where's Vera gone?' Marcus asked himself. 'Just when I needed her.'

There was nothing else for it; someone had to beat Mr Riley to it. The 'someone' had to be him. So off he set. As he passed Reception he shouted, 'Follow me, Angie – and you Brenda! You stand by to ring the police!' It was getting more like Agincourt every minute.

By then he was off down the corridor. He passed Mac, Head of Languages, who had come to the classroom door to find out what the noise was about.

'Mac, it's Adrian – Mr Wilkins. He might be being assaulted by a parent!' Mac joined the chase.

'Come with us,' cried Marcus again as he saw Dance teacher Jenny, floating along the cross-corridor. Jenny, not knowing precisely what was happening, tagged onto the rear. Marcus turned right and left the corridor via an outside door to take a shortcut across the playground. His growing team of helpers also turned right and followed behind.

Meanwhile Mac had noticed caretaker, Ted, with brush and pan, and told him Adrian had been attacked; Ted had yelled to Art teacher, Tabitha, whom he saw coming out of a cupboard in the corridor that he had it *on good authority* 'Adrian is being mortally wounded.' Tabitha whispered excitedly to her current heart-throb, Tim from Information Technology, who was also emerging from the cupboard, 'There's blood all over the gym floor'.

She then assured both her own class and two others that school was in lockdown and they should not move but should not panic either. Of course, they immediately did and Assistant Head, Muriel, had to take charge and bang on a desk to quieten them down.

Marcus and his cohort were now racing across the playground. It was now reminiscent of a scene from *The Pirates of Penzance*. The motley crew reached the main gymnasium door. No frothing Irishman had been spotted. Drat! He had beaten them to it. Marcus put up his hand. The cohort concertinaed into a milling phalanx and gathered round the door.

Marcus signalled for silence and tiptoed cautiously towards the male changing room door. As he was about to grasp the handle the door was flung open and there stood mighty Miss Cameron, Kelly Cameron, Head of Girls PE. Marcus and Kelly eyed each other. Miss Cameron's eye arched and eyebrows lifted as she peered first at Marcus and then at his bodyguard, two of whom appeared to be Caretaker Ted carrying a brush and pan like a cutlass and shield and behind him young assistant Caretaker Mildred brandishing a bristling yard brush and a galvanised bucket thrust in front of her, rather like a Roman scutum.

'What are you doing in the Boys changing room, Miss Cameron?' asked Marcus rather lamely. 'You shouldn't be in there, should you? The boys might be somewhat … dishevelled.'

'Goodness me, Headmaster. There's nothing in there I haven't seen before. If you provide a gym with such a daft layout you mustn't be surprised if we make our own rules. Anyway, that's not why you are here, is it?'

'No, it isn't! Follow me!' He waved his arm to his followers and swept past Miss Cameron. The whole legion burst in on fifty Year 10 boys completely naked, coming out of showers and going into showers, swishing towels around their bodies or someone else's body. Dancer Jenny pirouetted to take in the whole scene at one turn.

Marcus turned to his receptionist, Angie. 'Take note of what is going on, Miss Terry! I want every detail recorded.'

Receptionist Angie Terry let out the mildest of screams. Her hand went to her widening eyes but leaving sufficient gap between the first and second finger in order not to miss vital details.

'Now, where is he?' demanded Marcus, swivelling round to survey the whole room.

'Where's who?' asked Gupta, whose towel was held so low that Marcus felt obliged to signal him to lift it up before he answered. 'Mr Wilkins, of course, and a parent, a Mr Riley.'

'Oh,' said Gupta, mistaking Marcus's signal and whipping off his towel and rubbing his tousled hair. Angie's eyes opened wider. 'They left here just before you arrived, sir.' Marcus stifled a gasp.

'That's what I was about to tell you, Headmaster,' said Miss Cameron, 'if you had not pushed past me in that unseemly fashion. Mr Wilkins has taken Mr Riley up to the staffroom work area for a ... chat. He asked me to keep an eye on the boys getting to their next lessons. I could have told you all that if you had paused.'

Marcus looked round while his brain caught up with him. 'A chat! So Riley wasn't beating the living daylights out of Mr Wilkins then?'

'I have no idea what you are suggesting, Headmaster. They seemed as thick as thieves to me. Laughing and smiling they were.'

'Laughing and smiling? Laughing? And smiling? Is that what they were doing?' Marcus looked around. His legionnaires obviously wanted a lead. 'Thank you, ladies and gentlemen. It seems that our prompt action has averted a disaster.'

Marcus left his crew looking bewildered and bounded off to the staff workroom. There he found Head of PE and Mr Riley and Deputy Vera, seated round a coffee table, sipping tea. Nobody appeared to be shouting at anybody else.

Marcus stood in the doorway. 'I do apologise for—'

Vera cut him off. 'I have just explained to Mr Riley, Headmaster, that you were doing playground duty. We have also explained the school's policy of "no corporal punishment".'

'Ah, yes. I must assure you, Mr Riley, that the school does not condone any...' Marcus began.

And we've *explained* that there was *no* corporal punishment administered to his son.' Vera's teeth were gritted and her voice shrill.

'What? No .... You have what? So what was it then?' Marcus felt that he was fast losing control, unaware that he had already lost it .

Adrian Wilkins now joined in. 'I have explained to Mr Riley, Sir, that young Riley simply never turned up for PE at all. He just left the school – disappeared. I did try telephoning you, Headmaster, but you were engaged – trying to get hold of me, I think – so I sent a note to the office.'

124

'Yes, I put it into your in-tray,' said Angie, who had now caught up and was standing behind Marcus. 'While you were on the phone.'

'Oh … right … Well, may I suggest Mr Riley that you pursue the matter a little further with your son. In a friendly sort of way. Bring him back to school and we'll sort it all out, eh?'

To his credit Mr Riley did just that, and a day later the errant son apologised to the PE teacher, the Head, and Vera. There had been no corporal punishment. Bernard owned up to simply bunking off school because he did not like PE, and in particular he absolutely hated changing into shorts and plimsolls in a cold changing room. After his session with father, he felt more inclined to 'give PE a try.' Marcus let him off with a mild caution. Life returned to normal.

Next day, at their morning meeting, Vera asked casually 'Why haven't you punished Bernard at all for breaking the rules? It might make things difficult for staff, you know. They deserve an explanation.'

Marcus ran his hand through his hair – as he did when harassed. 'I'll explain it at the staff meeting this afternoon. I'll give them a good reason – but I'll tell you the real reason, Vera.' He paused and gathered his thoughts.

'The truth is that I also hated PE in my youth and I, too, bunked off school one day, and once it dawned on me that Bernard's sin was my sin – well I just couldn't be hypocritical. I know you'll tell me that my position is different now, Vera, but that's the truth of it, and having let Bernard off I feel as though a weight has been lifted from me. Forgive me if you can.'

Vera said nothing. She got up and made for the door. Marcus watched her in sadness. She turned and faced him. 'Let me just say this, Marcus. I did just the same when I was a teenager – I am so glad you did what you did.'

PLAYTIME

The Play's the Thing

School plays, school musicals, school choirs, school orchestras, school clubs – they all play an important part in the diurnal school roundabout. But none gives as much opportunity for unintentional humour as the school Nativity Play. A company specialising in legal support for schools used its monthly circular to report to its client schools the legal perils of Christmas-time activities.

It is well known that parents can be easily aggrieved and even litigious when schools seem to err. But a new feature was evident recently at Much Knowing Primary School where its precocious pupils have become aware of the endless and profitable possibilities of litigation. They found fertile ground in the annual nativity play.

The first sign of impending trouble came after the Head's announcement at morning assembly that Simeon would not be continuing with the part of the Archangel Gabriel because extorting sweets from Year 3 pupils for unspecified angelic favours was unseasonably naughty.

Simeon waited just one day before delivering his solicitor parents' brief letter suggesting that either Simeon was reinstated, or the question of substantial damages for defamation might have to be explored.

At this point the Head took sick leave.

The music teacher was left in sole charge of the production. At the next rehearsal Delilah (aged nine) broke into uncontrollable tears when told that she could certainly not play one of the three Kings, as these were boys' parts. In between sobs she managed to indicate her intricate knowledge of the scope of Part 6 of the Equality Act 2010. Her suggestion that the dressing gowns worn by the kings could equally well be worn by girls was considered highly plausible. So, Shane now became ex-King Balthasar and was consigned to the back row of the choir of angels, where he demonstrated his disgruntlement by flicking stardust all over the front-of-stage flock of sheep and the attendant shepherds. In this he was aided by shepherd Wayne, who considered the role to be 'cissy'. He had purloined the make-up box – 'for added interest', he pleaded – and had already been prevented from branding the Year 2 sheep with red and black stars.

However, Wayne and Shane's dastardly act was spotted from the back of the hall by the Head who had now been restored to health by a large slug of yellowish liquid kept for medicinal purposes in his desk drawer. She rushed forward, grabbed hold of both boys, and cuffed them about the ears – 'Only gently,' she claimed at his subsequent disciplinary hearing, following complaints by Wayne who was the most aggrieved of the two.

Shane considered he had a better chance of success and financial reward under the Abolition of Corporal Punishment Act 1997 which made corporal punishment a criminal offence, with the enticement of potential civil litigation on the back of it. The case is pending but the Head is relying on the defence that her actions prevented a greater hurt. She is not hopeful.

The calm that descended at this point was shattered by a dreadful scream from the front end of the donkey. Eponymous Joseph, feeling bored with the inactivity at his end of the stable, had shoved a candle from the crib up the backside of the animal. Rear-end Darren leapt in the air causing front-end Erasmus to fall off the stage, dragging the rear end with him. Both suffered cuts and bruises. The writ when it arrived mentioned the Health and Safety at Work Etc Act 1974, the Occupiers Liability Act 1984, and 'in loco parentis', citing the school for negligence in not taking into account the propensities of small boys to do unmentionable things with attractive lethal objects

The Head returned to sick leave.

But in the end, as these things are wont to do, the actual performance for parents passed by peacefully and to great acclaim, amassing a large amount for the school fund from ticket sales, complete with a glass of mulled wine (provided by the PTA). The photographs in the local newspaper were pleasing too. The Head felt she was entitled to a welcome Christmas break.

It was a week after the end of term when she opened a further letter from Simeon's parents regretting that she had not asked them whether they consented to an image of their Simeon appearing in the newspaper and enquiring (as a matter of interest) whether the school had a licence under the Licensing Act 2003 for charging for entrance tickets accompanied by alcohol. She felt justified in passing that one to the trustees, but on Christmas Eve she received another letter, this time from the publishers of the carols pointing out the huge compensation they might be seeking, if she could not adequately explain the school's failure to obtain their permission for the performance of their carols, and for breach of copyright.

She went off sick again.

Fair Titania

Some schools, having performed their plays and musicals or orchestral and choral concerts in school, are brave enough to take them abroad. Marcus Brampton's memory of the Market Upabit School's first thespian venture across the Channel has remained with him. He recounted his memories at the reunion in The Babbling Brook.

Our reputation for joint performances with foreign schools all began with my accepting an invitation from our exchange school in Western France to perform *A Midsummer Night's Dream* in the town theatre. We accepted, on condition that the Loudun lycée students would undertake to study the play, fill the stage with walk-on parts, and augment the small orchestra that played a significant role in our production. Their enthusiastic agreement led to our tradition of not performing 'to' our foreign hosts, but 'with' them. It lasted for the next twenty-three years, biennial productions performed at home and away, across Europe and in the United States.

As Headteacher, I naturally felt it incumbent on me to lead the party: an act of sacrifice in the eyes of a few discerning colleagues, a bit of a freebie for the Head according to others. I am not in a position to judge – only to remark that all the tours were in the school holidays, and all required, therefore, considerable commitment from staff, as well as from a group of parents who joined in the choruses and orchestras. Generations of students have cause to thank this small army of extras.

In the very first year of the adventure, the year of *A Midsummer Night's Dream*, we performed as requested in the town theatre. But while we were there we were invited to take the production to an old twelfth-century Abbey, in which a cultural centre was being established.

At the time of our visit, the old Abbey also housed an 'open prison'. During our daytime rehearsals the sixty-strong cast was allowed to rove around the grounds where some of the prisoners had been detailed to sweep leaves off the paths. The sight of such a phalanx of teenagers parading round the formal garden in flimsy Tudor dress was too much for the prisoners.

The sweeping got slower and slower, the piles of leaves got smaller and smaller, the prisoners got closer and closer to the actors. But not only did the brushing get slower and sloppier, the prisoners were prolonging the work and therefore the time needed to complete the job and to remain in the vicinity of the actors, by vigorously shaking more leaves off the trees! Consequently, the leaves remaining on the paths always outweighed the ones swept away!

Doing all their shenanigans out of sight of the warders was an example of high management skills by the prisoners; not surprising really, since most of the inmates were there because of crimes of fraud and extortion. Their enterprise only stopped when spotted by an eagle-eyed Head Warder – a disappointing end to what the gaolers saw as unacceptable conduct, but what the inmates saw as highly professional activity.

During the performance that night disaster struck. The lad playing a hilarious Bottom had the misfortune, in his comic enthusiasm, to trip over backstage during the interval and suffer a mild concussion on the hard stone floor. He was packed off to medical care. But what to do now? There was a large audience of French academics, parents and students and we were only halfway through! There was still the bower scene with Bottom transmogrified into an ass, and about to be kissed by Titania. My colleague and stage manager, Don, was in no doubt what had to be done. He thrust the papier-mâché ass's head at me and said, in a voice that brooked no argument, *'You've* got to do it!'

'What? I can't do it!' I yelled, backing off.

'Oh yes you can. You're the only one who can do it! You're the producer – and the show must go on! So, here's Bottom's head, and here's a copy of the script.'

He plonked a tatty copy of the Penguin edition into my hands. There was clearly no arguing. In any case, Don had disappeared to tell the audience, aided by our language teacher, what had happened and what they were now going to get – 'a well-known actor' who had kindly stepped in, and who would now be playing the part aided by a copy of the script. Well at least half of that was correct.

So, at the start of the second half the audience was going to be treated to a quite different ass embracing and cuddling Titania, while at the same time holding a copy of the script! I was comforted by the knowledge that at least the new Bottom's identity was shielded by the outsized paper head!

And that is what happened – but not without a last-minute crisis! I crept onto the set and settled down in the bower, adjusting the ass's head, and uttering a silent prayer. All should have been well. But this was a school production! When Titania, a sixteen-year-old Year 11 girl, was just about to go on stage she saw who was taking over. She let out an audible gasp and turned to Don.

'I'm not kissing the Headmaster! I'm not going on! Definitely not!'

Another crisis. But Don was not a man to mess with. 'O yes you are,' he hissed. '*This* show goes on – and so do you!' With that he picked up the reluctant Titania and hurled her onto the stage just before the curtain went up.

Meanwhile I was lying in the bower idly wondering where Titania was and blissfully ignorant of the scuffle off-stage. The next thing I knew was a bundle of rags landing on top of me, and a startled Titania whispering through gritted teeth, 'OK. Let's get on with it, Sir.'

And so get on with it we did.

Of course, she carried on being brilliant. Rather too amorous at times, methought! She began to revel in her new-found role as mentor to the Head. She led me round the stage in moves that had never been rehearsed or even contemplated, and at the apex of our love affair she whispered, 'Oh just get rid of that book and just snog, Sir. Make it up – you know it well enough.' She took charge, and, as I said, she was brilliant.

As for me, well, let's say that I was right to have forbidden anyone from taking photos! I mean – one has a reputation to maintain! Nonetheless, I believe some staff did snap as many photos as they could. I have never seen them – but I know they still exist! There are some things in life, it appears, that remain desirable curiosities for all sorts of reasons.

Mens Sana, in Corpore Sano

The school Sports Day has been an important date in many schools'
calendars from time immemorial. They are usually festive as well as
sporting occasions, but with so many pupils to shuffle, so many
parents to organise and so many important guests to impress they
can be fraught with danger for the inexperienced – or plain unwary.

The annual Sports Day at Much Knowing Primary School –
that hotbed of primary jurisprudential learning, where eleven-
year-olds had learned far too much from their professional
guardians – began, as it always did, with a welcome speech by
the Head, recently returned to her post following a long
convalescence after the trauma of last year's nativity play. For
the time being she was in radiant health. She announced that,
for this year's Sports Day, a number of restrictions would be
placed on the parents' teams in the annual parent/pupil
competitions, following 'certain incidents' last year. Parents
were only allowed to serve underarm during the annual tennis
competition, and fathers were obliged to tie themselves to
other children's mothers in the three-legged race, partners
having been drawn by lot. She felt that this would be fairer to
the pupil teams. The parents on the other hand were not sure
that their children needed any more advantages.

When the Head sat down, Head Girl Beatrice gave the
official thanks. She did this very sweetly, drawing encouraging
smiles from her Headmistress, until she got to the last
paragraph. In her carefully crafted peroration, she expressed
her regret that the school appeared to have breached the
Equality Act's age-related discrimination legislation, which
outlaws treating someone worse than another person in a
similar position because of their age. Hearing this, the Head
had a mild fainting fit and had to be revived by the Chair of the
Board of Trustees waving a white handkerchief over her face.

Beatrice pottered off amidst enthusiastic applause from fellow pupils, leaving the Head clutching the sides of her seat and explaining in a hoarse voice to the Chair of the Board that there could be no possible basis to the claim. She was sure she had read somewhere that students are not protected from age discrimination at school. However, she suggested nervously that it might be worth the trustees spending a bob or two to gain Counsel's clarification of the point. Inwardly she was thinking, 'It's going to be one of those days.' Indeed it was.

There was already a controversy in the Year 6 hurdle race which Imogen had won easily, avoiding actually jumping the hurdles by simply running round them. She was immediately disqualified by Head of Girls PE, Ms Strapping. Ms Strapping then had to face the wrath of Imogen's solicitor mother, who pointed out that there was no instruction to the competitors as to how they should approach the hurdles and therefore runners were free to run the race how they liked. It was clearly much safer to run round the hurdles than leap over them, she opined. In any case, she had not seen any risk assessment nor risk management plan. Perhaps Ms Strapping would oblige?

The Head of PE would not. She was indignant. She protested that everyone knew how you had to run a hurdle race, and in any case her decision was final. Imogen mater marched off to the tea tent to seek out the Head, vowing that the school 'had not heard the last of this'. How could the school punish a pupil who was simply following the school motto of 'cognito ad salutem' ('knowledge leads to victory')?

Further shenanigans were also taking place at the shot-putting ring. Miss Hardy, a newly qualified Class 1 teacher, full of enthusiasm and idealistic inexperience of sports days, was put in charge of the boys under 11 competition. To create a lively and memorable event she ordered Simeon, Zachariah and Jim of Rossini House to stand at the landing end in order to throw back the shot balls after they had been thrown from the putting circle by the boys of Offenbach House.

Samson, the school champion and a bit of a bully, was first to go. He saw his chance for a bit of fun, flexed his muscles and let fly – straight at his nearest rival standing innocently in the landing area, Simeon. Inevitably the shot circumscribed a perfect parabola and landed squarely on Simeon's big toe. The victim's ear-splitting yelp caused Year 5 Emily to miss her footing in the high jump and crash into the bar, damaging her left femur and denying her the chance to emulate her older sister's feat of clearing one metre before her tenth birthday. She was distraught; mother was livid; father set off for the tea tent to join the queue seeking a word with the Head.

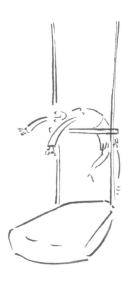

He was just behind Simeon's dad, who being a criminal law barrister, knew nothing about civil law but was pretty sure a shot ball on the big toe was prima facie potential negligence. He was determined to tell the Head that 'it was nothing short of criminal to put an untrained, inexperienced teacher in charge of such a deadly pursuit.'

The Head countered, from a sedentary position, by protesting that it was 'a pure accident'. She remembered from the court case following last Christmas's nativity play affair that judges had time and time again followed the dictum of Lord Justice Scrutton as long ago as 1932 that 'no schoolmaster in the world can prevent a naughty boy doing naughty things on some occasions'. She tentatively offered this as 'a satisfactory defence'. Barrister dad was not appeased and made that plain. The Head had to go and lie down.

Meanwhile the inter-house soccer final was hotting up. Wagner House was holding on to a narrow lead from Verdi House when Duane retaliated violently to a cynical trip by Erasmus Knott as he burst through the centre. Referee Mr Goven (Mikey) quickly stepped in and separated the boys by grabbing hold of their shoulders and thrusting them apart. When they continued to aim blows at each other he shook their shoulders and warned, 'If I catch you doing that again I will ban you from future matches.'

'Ha, ha,' cried Erasmus, whose wiliness stretched further than mere tripping, 'You've just punished us by shaking our shoulders, and corporal punishment was banished by the Education Act 1986. Wait till I tell my dad, Judge Knott.' When informed of this threat the Head, currently stretched out on her study sofa, added an icepack to her aching forehead.

At least, thought the senior staff, nothing can go wrong with the annual inter-house cross-country race. The start was in the hands of old hand, and former Territorial Army officer, Charles Burton-Latimer. Each year he used the same routine. For him there was no need for a starting pistol. For thirty years he had clapped two pieces of wood together with a loud bang to signify the start. It was all quite simple. No need for new-fangled aids. But this year rebellious Boadicea Warliker and her tribe of pals were bent on revenge for some unspecified hurt by 'Clobber Burton'. Or maybe it was just the high spirits that inevitably accompany school sports days. Anyway, Clobber stood in front of the mass of 150 runners and yelled, as he had always done, 'You will only start when I clap my clappers like this,' and demonstrated by bringing the two bits of wood together in a sharp 'crack'.

At this, without a moment's hesitation, the whole 150 set off as one, led by Boadicea with an ear-piercing cry of 'Olly, olly, olly – go, go, go!' The Charge of the Young Brigade rapidly bore down on, and then swarmed all over, a paralysed Clobber. He was left behind squirming in the grass, waving his clappers furiously above his prostrate body, crying, 'I haven't clapped my clappers yet!'

The dust settled behind the disappearing brigade of foot soldiers. Bright little Sharon from Year 6 sauntered across to Clobber, looked down at the forlorn body and consoled him, or at least she thought she did, by pointing out that he could always invoke the anti-harassment law. She told him that harassment occurs when someone makes you feel humiliated, offended or degraded.

'You look pretty degraded to me,' she added. 'I would definitely sue the school if I were you.' She then wandered off to watch the tennis.

The Head who was feeling very much better after a good tea suffered a serious lapse when informed of the latest development. She retired to lie down again.

French Cricket

It was at the next reunion at 'The Babbling Brook' that 'Dan' Dare
persuaded Rosalind Brampton to tell her story about her friend,
Felicity.

'You're a bit quiet, Ros,' said Dan.

'Just a bit whacked, Dan. We only got back from the south of France
yesterday, visiting our old friends Felicity and Rupert. Felicity is just
as volatile as ever – she never stops! But that is just how we
remember her when she first came over to England, where she met
Rupert, unbelievably on the cricket field.'

'You're intriguing us, Ros. Explain.'

You have to first understand that Felicity de la Valastière – Fifi,
– was the best thing that had happened to St Stephen's School
Languages Department for many a long year. It was not just
that she was, well, simply beautiful in the classical manner, but
she was vivacious, clever, witty, full of life. St Steve's had
hosted French Assistants for years, but not one like this. Never
had so many boys opted for French at A Level. Never had Sixth
Formers had to pass tests before being allowed to attend
Mademoiselle's conversation classes.

Each pupil had his own way of summarising her special
point of interest: the flashing of the smile, the shortness of the
skirt, the amplitude of the bosom, the length of the leg, the
Frenchness of her accent – all had their admirers.

The same went for the girls at the sister school, St Agnes's
down the road, where Fifi also took French conversation
lessons. Instead of being jealous, the girls revelled in the
modernity of style: the pixie hairstyle, the delicate mascara, the
sultry eye shadow, and the fetching use of lipstick, all of which
Mademoiselle brought into their daily round.

Fifi de la Valastière loved life and life loved her, and having admired the British ruggedness, the down-to-earth sturdiness and the laughter of the English Assistants who had spent a year at her Parisian lycée, she was now determined to find out as much as she could about England and zee Ee-nglish – and what could be more quintessentially English? Why cricket, of course. All the English Assistants she had ever met had told her so.

And that is why the St Stephen's Chaplain, the Reverend Aloysius Possington-Smythe, found her sitting alone on a bench watching the first school cricket match of the season, the annual Old Boys match. She may have been alone on the bench, but she was surrounded by a posse of Upper and Lower School boys, lolling about on the grass at her feet or by the side of the bench, all watching carefully, but discretely, Fifi's long legs as they crossed (frequently) right over left and left over right, waiting for the moment that this left and right interchange swung into action in the hope of a glimpse of thigh and perhaps a speck of white frill underneath the bright yellow pelmet that passed as a skirt.

They were disappointed. Like the view of France from Dover cliffs, the hoped-for sighting was so often thwarted by the swiftness of the changing clarity of scenery. Fifi was a skilled crosser of legs.

The Reverend Aloysius advanced and doffed his straw boater. 'Is this anyone's seat, Mam'selle?'

'Mais non,' smiled Felicity and edged further to her left. Aloysius settled down at the right-hand edge. It was his favourite bench. He could be caught sight of there at every first-eleven home match. Apart from his God, his Church, and his vast array of books and CDs, Aloysius loved cricket. He could not play the game to save his life. Poor eyesight and uncoordinated limbs prevented that, but goodness me, his knowledge of the game, its Laws (always a capital L), its tactics, its history, its personalities – all were at the chaplain's finger-tips. And the traditional start to the season was this School versus Old Boys match, which brought back to St

Stephen's all the old stars of bat and ball that had thrilled him over the years. However, he had to admit, in all the years of service to the school and devoted attendance at cricket matches he had never sat next to anyone half as attractive as Mademoiselle de la Valastière. Felicity, ever gregarious, turned to the chaplain.

'Me-e-ster Reverend. You are a great cricketer, no?'

Aloysius chuckled. 'No, ma'am, I love the game, but I do not play it very well. Oh, and by the way, call me Chaplain – it is so much more, err, friendly, personal, if you see what I mean.'

Felicity was puzzled. 'Chaplain? Zat is your name?'

'No, no. I am the school chaplain. My name is Aloysius Possington-Smythe, but people just refer to me as "Chaplain".'

'If Aloysius is your name, zen I call you Aloysius. No, I shall be even more friendly, more personal. I will call you Al. You must call me Fifi. That is what my friends and family call me, so you must, too.'

'I say,' murmured Aloysius, or Al as he now was, running a finger round his dog collar which was now feeling decidedly sweaty. 'I say – I'm not sure such, err, intimacy is proper at St Stephen's, you know.'

'No-one will know, Al. It is between you and me. It is our little secret.'

'I say—' was all Aloysius could say.

Now, explain to me thees game, Al, thees cricket.'

This was safer ground, thought Aloysius, but he was not going to fall into the trap of trying to explain the game to a foreigner. He knew the pitfalls. It might be 50 years ago, but the famous tea-towel summary still stuck with him.

> You have two sides, one out in the field and one in.
> Each man that's in the side that's in goes out, and when he's out he comes in and the next man goes in until he's out.
> When they are all out, the side that's out comes in and the side that's been in goes out and tries to get those

coming in, out. Sometimes you get men still in and not out.

When a man goes out to go in, the men who are out try to get him out, and when he is out he goes in and the next man in goes out and goes in.

There are two men called umpires who stay out all the time and they decide when the men who are in are out. When both sides have been in and all the men have been out, and both sides have been out twice after all the men have been in, including those who are not out, that is the end of the game.

Oh no, Aloysius was certainly not going down that road! He played safe, a straight bat. 'It is far too complex to explain in a short time, mam'selle , err. Fifi. I'll tell you what is happening and answer any questions you might have.'

'Zat is very good. So, Aloyisius, why are all zee players wearing white clothes, hein? Eez eet a symbol zey are all zee virgins – like zee vestal virgins? And zose two men in white coats and straw hats, zey are symbolising zee archangels, non?'

Aloysius, ever kind and indulgent, smiled and raised a hand in some kind of blessing. 'In a way, they are, Mam'selle. They make all the decisions about who is in and who is out.'

'Where is in and where is out?' said Fifi looking around.

Alarm bells rang. Aloysius could see the labyrinth of tea-towel explanation looming.

'You are making things far too complicated for me, Mam … Fifi. Look here, just listen to me, and I will describe what is happening and tell you why.' That was meant as a generous offer. It was a mistake. At that moment one of the Old Boys fielders sauntered over and stood in front of them, obscuring Fifi's view. Fifi pounced.

'Excusez-moi, Monsieur. Please sit down. I cannot see what is going on.'

'Don't speak to the fielder, Mam'selle. He's playing! He cannot sit down.'

144

'Oh là là! Quel dommage! 'Ee has got a sore derrière, yes? Ze poor boy.'

'No, he does not have a sore bottom, or a sore anything else. He is here to see if he can make a catch out in the long grass.'

Fifi stared incredulously at young and handsome Rufus Atherton-Cooke, the Old Boys wily spin-bowler and last year's school captain.

'Mon dieu! 'Ee want to make a catch, in zee long grass?' She stared longingly at Atherton-Cooke. 'Ee is very beau – in an English sort of way. 'Ee would be a good catch, I think – ee can catch me, non?' She did not wait for Aloysius's answer. She rose to her feet and hailed the unsuspecting Rufus.

'Ere M'sieur. I too know about zee catching. And I know all about zee long grass—' Fifi took a step forward.

Reverend Aloyisius put out his hand to stop her.

'No, no Mam'selle Fifi! Don't do that. You will interfere with his movement.'

Fifi halted and stared pityingly at young Rufus, and then sat down again.

'I should think 'ees sore derrière will also interfere with 'ees movement. But if I cannot get to 'im, then 'ow is he going to catch anyone in zee long grass?'

Aloysius rubbed his chin and considered how to describe a catch.

'Look, he makes his catch by putting his hands up—'

'Sacré bleu!' cried Fifi, pressing her skirt tightly to her legs. 'Ee does what, M'sieur!?'

The good Reverend, now in some confusion and wishing to save the situation, raised his arms.

'He puts his hands up, mam'selle, like this, and cups the ball in his hands so.'

'Ee likes ze balls? So, 'ee is homosexual, then?'

Aloysius was at a loss. He looked around wildly for help. None was available.

'Beg pardon, Mam'selle? What on earth do you mean?' Aloysius felt a worrying perplexity with the different national and cultural perceptions growing in him. 'I do not know if he is gay or no. He might be, or he might not .'

'Ah, I see, 'Ee is androgynous?'

'What are you talking about? His sexuality doesn't come into it! It doesn't matter!'

Fifi raised her voice a decibel. 'M'sieur! If I am going into zee long grass wiz 'im, it matters to me!'

Aloysius grabbed Fifi's arm and pointed towards the pitch. 'Look, let's start again. The ball I am talking about is the one the bowler has got in his hand and is bowling at the boy's stumps. He is aiming to hit the stump. you can see him bowling throwing it, no. I mean, non?'

'Zere is no need to grab my arm, M'sieur Al.' Fifi felt aggrieved at the suddenness of the Chaplain's physical contact. I can understand perfectly well.'

She held Aloysius's arm now and pointed to the fielders. 'Ze man 'ere. 'Ee is trying to hit zat boy zere in ze stump, eh?'

'Yes, good. That's roughly right.'

She shook her head. 'Monsieur Aloysius. 'Itting in zee stump will be very painful, n'est-ce pas? It could ruin eez chances of a catch now or always. Does 'ee not know zat? 'Ave you not told eem?'

'No, no, Fifi, a stump is not a euphemism for a … err … delicate part of the anatomy. Those are the stumps you see. The

147

three bits of wood!' Aloysius was about to grab her arm again but thought better of it.

'I see eet. I always see eet. But what is zat boy doing wiz ze piece of wood in ees 'and?

'Ah,' said the Chaplain brightening up. 'That's easy. He is trying to hit the bowler's balls as hard as he can.'

''Ee is *what*, Monsieur? Mon dieu! 'Ee, too, is trying to bash balls? Quelle horreur! I did not realise what a violent game zis cricket i. It is no wonder we French do not play ze cricket.'

Fifi sank back into the bench, eyes agog, muttering to herself, 'Quelle folie ce pays, c'est vraiment remarquable.'

The bowling changed ends and the fielders began to take up fresh positions.

'And why, Monsieur Chaplain, are all zese men walking around zee field?'

Aloysius thought hard, trying to work out whether he was about to say something else that he would regret.

'Zey, I mean, *they* are the fielders whose job it is to field the ball, and to prevent the batsmen from running from one end of the pitch to the other.' That seemed innocuous enough.

Fifi contemplated this new knowledge.

'Hm. Since zee cricket ees such a violent game would it not be easier to tackle ze boys in ze middle like ze rugby football, and hit them with their balls before they could get up, hein?

Aloysius cleared his throat. 'Oh no, that would be quite unacceptable – illegal, in fact!'

'And zee hitting of zee balls with a big piece of wood ees not illegal? Very strange. What is zee difference, Monsieur? Eh?'

The chaplain's mouth gaped. It was poppycock, but he could not find words to say why.

'Because ... because ... well ... because the game has to be played according to the Laws and it is the Law that bowlers can throw a ball at the batsman only from behind "the crease".' Oh Lord, he thought to himself, I must not get into explaining the crease! 'You see, Fifi, it has to be bowled according to the Laws of Cricket, or otherwise the bowler has a "no ball" against his name.'

'Ze bowler might lose eez balls? Ees zat what you are telling me Al, in your English way? Quelle délicatesse.'

The six-ball over was completed and the fieldsmen moved again.

'Look, zay move again. 'Ow do they know where to go?'

Once again Aloysius felt on safer ground. Another mistake. 'Let me explain,' he said enthusiastically. The captain of the fielding side, which is the Old Boys, puts the fielders where the bowler expects the batsmen to hit the ball. You see here, this bowler has got a fine leg.'

A fine leg. Oh là là! I cannot see eet because of eez trousers. Perhaps, monsieur you could persuade 'im to take them off. It should not be a problem for a man trying to make a catch. Ee could show off eez fine legs.'

But the Reverend was not listening. He was taking an intense interest in the field placing, as students of the game do.

'By Jove! He's got a square leg, too,' he muttered half to himself. He was jolted out of his study by a loud exclamation next to him.

'Sacré bleu! Ee 'as a square leg as well as a fine leg? Le pauvre garçon.' Fifi stared at Mr Meldrum, the Old Boys' oldest player, now about to bowl from the pavilion end, his silver hair flowing over his shoulders. 'So, you 'ave able bodied players and ze disabled and ze very old men and ze very young boys playing each other. That is very noble, Al. Noblesse sauvage. Eet is typically British, I think.'

Aloysius stared at her. He had no idea what she was talking about, so he chose to ignore her murmured admiration. That was a mistake, too.

'And now he has a long leg,' said Al, pointing vaguely in that direction. 'He has put Rupert Grafton-Fitzpatrick there. That is very strange, but it could be a coup, you know. A fine leg, a square leg and a long leg. Not normal at all but could be brilliant.'

'You are telling me, M'sieur, zis long leg and zee square leg ees very abnormal. What a man! I admire him, M'sieur.'

'And so you should. Rupert has just bowled a maiden over.'

149

''Ee 'as? And I did not see 'im!'

'He bowled six maidens last match.'

'Six? Six maidens!' She looked admiringly across to where Rupert Grafton- Fitzpatrick was guarding the long leg area. 'Quel homme! Quel taureau! C'est un homme que j'aimerais connaître – bientôt. I zink 'ee and I will get on, do you not think so, Al?'

'Don't get too enthusiastic, young lady,' Aloysius chuckled. 'He also dropped a dolly!'

'He did? Ze poor man. Was she not good for him?'

'It was terrible. Fell right into his arms and then it went right through to the ground.'

Fifi eyed Rupert wistfully. 'I would not let 'im drop me from his arms, Your Reverence.'

The umpire called 'over' and took the bails off the stumps. The Old Boys moved towards the pavilion for the tea break.

'Zee archangel, 'ee has said the match is over, Al?'

'Not quite. This is the tea interval. Half-time, you might say. Let's go and join them.'

The chaplain marched off towards the pavilion with Fifi in tow.

'I'll introduce you to Rupert – the one you rather liked who is good with maidens. I know he'll be scoring for the Old Boys' team during their innings. He may let you score with him.'

Fifi squealed with delight, stood on tiptoe and gave Aloysius a big smacking kiss on the cheek.

'Zank you, my favourite Reverend Chaplain Aloysius Al. I know how to score wiz zee Rupert in zee long grass! I go immédiatement.'

The Reverend Possington-Smythe stood transfixed in the middle of the field. With his hand stroking his cheek, muttering contentedly to himself. 'I say ...I say ...'

Oops, La, La!

Being in charge of school parties abroad is an onerous duty. One wonders why any teacher agrees to take part. But they do, thousands of them, not for any extra remuneration but for the sheer joy of being with young people in a different and often challenging environment. They are organised with meticulous care and for many people, of any age, they are the defining memory of school for the rest of their lives, definitely a major subject in any school reunion. Marcus Brampton recounted in The Babbling Brook stories he had been told of such trips abroad.

I heard once of an incident that happened on a school trip to a holiday centre on the north French coast. The Headmaster was in charge. He dutifully told all his eleven-year-old charges not to jump down a sandy dune above the beach as it was unstable and therefore dangerous, as well as being a disturbance for others using the beach. A clear prohibition.

During the morning, sitting in his beach deckchair surveying the shoreline activity, he saw two boys doing just what he had ordered them not to do – they were running up the dune and jumping down, with great showers of fine sand polluting the air, and particularly his own air.

This really was not on. He had brought them all this way, looked after them coddled them, imbued the need for safety first at all times and concern for others and this is how they repaid his care. Really.

Incensed at the indiscipline, he rushed along the beach, scrambled up the dune, grabbed hold of both of them, yelling loudly at both of them in his fury. The kids started crying and gesticulating wildly.

'Stop that blubbering!' he demanded. 'You've done wrong, been caught, now stop and learn.'

151

He stopped shaking them, let go of their arms and stood firmly in front of them wagging his finger.

'I will not have such behaviour, do you hear, eh?' No answer. One small tearful boy suddenly bolted down the beach. The others watched him go and then set off after him.

'Come back!' yelled the Head. 'How dare you!'

At this point his colleague who had tried unsuccessfully to intervene but had slithered back down the dune finally got to the top and grabbed hold of him, 'Sir, Sir, hold on, Sir!'

'What is it, Fortesque?'

'Actually, Headmaster, they're *not* ours. They're local French boys from the town!'

In the distance, down the beach, they could see a small boy pointing in their direction and a large father in beret and shorts getting up from his deckchair.

A Terminal Incident

On another occasion a young teacher, who had only been on one previous trip, was put in charge of a group of thirteen-year-olds on a day trip by bus and ferry to Calais. She knew all about breaking groups into small cells with an adult or senior student in charge, checking groups at motorway stops, ensuring there were sufficient comfort stops. Check, check, check.

Everything went extremely well until the coach rolled into the Dover Ferry Terminal. The ferry was just fifty yards away; their coach was in a line of other coaches and would be loaded in forty minutes. They were right next to some toilets, so she allowed a handful of students to nip to the loo. Just half a dozen. She counted them out at the front of the bus, and counted them in.

There was no need to shout down the bus asking if everyone was back, but she did anyway.

'Yes. Yes. Yes.' A few desultory voices because everyone was excited about the coach moving into the belly of the boat.

Content that the first part of her 'trial by school party' was successfully negotiated, she sat back and let out a large sigh of relief and contentment.

'Well done,' whispered her admiring male deputy leader.

It was only after she had downed the promised noggin and the ferry had picked up speed outside the harbour wall that a message came over the tannoy for Miss Smith to go to the Purser's office. It was then, and only then, at the ship's Purser's office that she learned that little Gertie was still on the quayside at Dover and would be joining the group on the next boat!

'Aaaarrgggghh,' cried Miss Smith.

'O Lor',' cried her male companion.'How can that be?'

153

The Purser who was listening in with a sympathetic smile said, 'We experience a lot of this kind of thing, Miss. Could I venture to ask if the bus has a door in the centre or rear, as well as one at the front?'

'Yeaaaarrrggghhh,' cried Miss Smith in response.

'O Lorrrrrr',' echoed her deputy.

'You can be sure that is where little Gertie got off and not on. Happened before – many times,' he sighed.

For the rest of the trip there were long, supervised queues at motorway stops and Gertie got her own private escort, with not another single incident to mar the experience.

Once bitten, twice very, very vigilant.

A Good Idea at the Time

And then there were 'the Nuns'. Marcus Brampton paused as he contemplated his next vivid memory. Ah, yes, the nuns. A painful memory, but one which, in all conscience, I am duty-bound to recount out of deference to, and as a warning to all who are arrogant enough or dare to advise others on 'their good idea for a school visit'.

I was commissioned by a well-known publisher of catalogues and handbooks to write a 'handbook' for school trip organisers, explaining the law, the rules and the best practice that was currently available. The impetus for this was a largish tome on the subject published by the government, the Department's guidance to school trip organisers. My own 'pocket book' was meant to be complementary, a little succinct something that leaders could take with them on the trip. It also contained extensive descriptions of the premier school trip destinations in the UK – London, obviously, but also Cambridge, Oxford, York, Warwick. I decided to split it regionally and give lots of contact information as well as descriptions of the venue. This was in the days before the internet or websites and so all information that eventually appeared was inevitably with a wing and a prayer as it was automatically out-of-date as soon as the book went to print.

Nevertheless, it proved popular with school trip companies, who usually gave copies free to organisers – so popular that eventually it was translated into French, Spanish, Italian and German, and, as I look at the different editions in front of me today, I feel a touch of satisfaction – nay pride– that they were all my own work. Except the translations, of course! I know my limitations, or most of them. Nevertheless, I was caught out by the Belgian Nuns.

One of the 'clever' things I did, which had not been done before, or has not been done since for that matter, was to list theatres, cinemas, cafés, restaurants, night clubs, etc that appealed to teenage groups and which were safe to visit in evenings. I not only had the support of the regional tourist boards but the police, too, who in many instances were prepared to indicate not where to go, but where not to go.

All went well for the first couple of years, and then in the third year my euphoria was rudely interrupted. My managing editor sent me a laconic note with a copy of a letter attached. 'Read this and send a possible and credible reply – soonest.'

The attached letter started benignly enough, 'Monsieur, j'ai apprécié votre guide de voyage.'

Okay, so she appreciated the travel guide. So what's the problem? Well, it did not take much reading to learn that Sister Angela had been in charge of a party of twenty teenage students from her convent school in northern Belgium for a summer holiday trip to London and Oxford. They had followed my guide, enjoyed the hints and advice offered, and had every confidence that the author's advice on evening venues would be as impeccable as the guidance on daytime destinations.

The group had collectively agreed that their last evening but one in London would be spent at a non-alcoholic bar and dance club that catered specially for teenagers on Thursday evenings. From my description it sounded a very good way to entertain the youngsters in a safe way in a turbulent foreign city. And indeed it was.

But the gap between my getting the evening schedule for the club and the publication of the guide was at least three months. Imagine, therefore, the surprise, the consternation of the Sisters of the Immaculate Conception, and the astonishment of their charges when the score of girls in somewhat staid convent school dress, accompanied by two nuns, walked into a bar full of ladies dressed as men and men dressed as ladies and some unclear which they were dressed as.

According to our nun correspondent they were well into the hubbub of the club before they cottoned on that Thursday nights were now 'LGBT' evenings – although at that time that term was unknown.

By this point in the letter I had blanched and wondered whether to read on. What was Sister Angela going to build up to, and was further trouble round the corner? And then I gulped and my hands stopped shaking. Sister Angela's letter continued, 'Je suis heureuse de vous dire que ...'

The Sister was 'happy' now, but about what? Well, she told us, the manager immediately recognised the mistake, urged them to stay, arranged an alcove where they could be together and asked a number of men and women to come over and engage them in conversation.

Oh Lor' I thought, they didn't, did they?

Yes, they did. They stayed, they mingled, and Sister Angela went on to say what a perfectly delightful evening of sensible conversation they had in halting English and even more hesitant French and non-existent Flemish.

Sister Angela, an astute teacher if ever there was one, noted that the unplanned evening improved the girls' English, added to their interest in London life, and increased their knowledge of 'la vie comme elle est vraiment' – life as it really is!

But, she continued – there is always a 'but', I groaned – Monsieur author should learn from this that things change. Shouldn't he consider telling readers to check details beforehand?

Yes, he must, and yes, they should.

Monsieur had himself learned a bit about life 'comme elle est vraiment'.

PERIOD THREE: WHAT HAPPENED AT SCHOOL TODAY?

Winner Takes All

Sometime around the 1980s, schools were encouraged to become 'entrepreneurial' to embrace the new culture of self-management and financial delegation and a status freer than ever from local authority control. Schools were bribed into embracing the new vogue by becoming 'specialist schools' and raising many thousands of pounds by their own 'business-like' efforts which were then matched by large grants from the government. Secondary schools had no option, really, but to give it a go, and thus become a specialist Business college or a Science college or a PE one or a Languages college. It was all heralded as the path to higher standards. The same underlying ethos prevails to this day, when all maintained schools, big and small, are expected to be self-managing academies like 'the great independent public schools' as one Minister enthusiastically hailed them. It was, and is, fertile ground for the entrepreneurial spirit to flourish at all levels. Some of the teenage spivs, wide-boys, market managers of the twentieth century were in their element, as Marcus Brampton recounted in The Babbling Brook.

Market Upabit student, Donny Dodge, 'the artful Dodge' I introduced you to in a previous story, was at home with this culture. His 'business' opponent was no other than our local MP. The story goes like this …

The local Member of Parliament for the Market Upabit constituency considered himself to be a blunt man, but a fair man, willing to give any person, business, or institution a fair crack of the whip. Well, that was his estimation of himself. His opponents considered him to be an unfair, bigoted cheat. But that's the way with party politics.

He was not a fan of comprehensive education, never had been. 'Can't see the point of putting clever types in the same school as thickies. That's a sure way of ensuring that neither cohort will succeed,' he was fond of saying to anyone who would listen. 'Don't know why we gave up on selection. Look what being selected has done for me!' His opponents never tired of replying, 'Yes, look.'

His favourite trick – to demonstrate the undeniable truth of his philosophy – was to take constituency guests to Market Upabit Academy and pick out the first small teenager he came across.

'Watch this,' he would say, nudging his guest. 'Just see how stupid they are.'

The MP happened to choose Donny Dodge, son of the owners of Market Upabit's Executive Motors garage and budding second-hand car salesman. He took a £1 coin and a 50p coin out of his pocket and offered them to Donny.

'Choose one,' said the MP. 'Go on and you can keep it. Just remember how generous your local MP is, eh?'

Donny smiled, nodded in his most obsequious manner, studied the coins carefully, scratched his chin and finally took the big one, the 50p.

'Thank you, Sir,' said Donny. 'Very kind of you, Sir. I shan't forget you. I promise.' He touched his forelock and ran off to the classroom.

The MP beamed. 'There you are,' he crowed. 'Proved! Never fails. Dear me, what do they teach them at these places?' He shook his head and took his companion's arm escorting him to my study, where he praised me on the school's outstanding games record and the last music concert and the colourful art work decorating the corridors and entrance area. Oh, and all the community work that had come to his attention. During the long, one-sided discussion, the guest excused himself and went off to the toilet. On the way back he caught sight of Donny in the corridor, standing outside a classroom door as Donny so frequently did.

'Excuse me young man, are you the pupil who just chose the 50p piece offered by your MP?'

'I am, Sir,' said Donny. 'And very generous of him it was. You can tell him I will always vote for him when I'm old enough. I certainly will.'

'Yes, all right. I'll do that. And tell me, do you really not know the difference between a 50p and a £1 coin?'

Though he tried to suppress it, a big grin spread over Donny's face. 'Of course I know which is which, Sir! I'm not that daft! But that bloke is always doing this, and when I see on the school's daily diary that he is coming into school I make sure I'm hanging around.'

The MP's friend looked puzzled. 'Well, why do you choose the 50p coin then?'

'Easy, Sir. The moment I choose the little £1 coin he'll stop playing the game!'

On the Rocks

Marcus Brampton told his friends in The Babbling Brook about a Yorkshire Junior School teacher who told him a story demonstrating, she said, the strength of character and directness of the 'typical' Yorkshire pupil. Whilst its verisimilitude cannot be confirmed, her story smacks of the truth of her observation.

Evie approached the teacher's desk.

'Miss, my mum told me the law says you don't have to have sex in primary schools. Do we have to have sex, Miss? It's scary.'

'It's not scary, Evie. Anyway, it's not "sex", it's "sex *education*". You will learn all sorts of interesting things.'

'What interesting things, Miss?'

'Err … lots. I haven't got time to go through them now. But, for example, you will learn how babies are made. That's interesting, isn't it?'

'I don't want to know that! Not if it has got anything to do with that serpent thing in the Bible, you know, in the Book of Genitals.'

'Book of *Genesis*, Evie.'

'That's what I said. Anyway the serpent is in that man's garden. Wound all round a tree. A serpent is a snake, isn't it, Miss? It gets the bloke and his girl. And she's named Evie, like me. That's why it's scary! Why does it have to be a snake, Miss? I'm scared of snakes. Can't it be a little lamb like the lamb God's got?'

'No, it can't Evie.'

'Why not? It would be a lot nicer. You can cuddle a lamb.'

'Because it's a story and the serpent is part of the story.'

'Well, if it is a story it can be changed. You're always asking us to write our own endings to stories. So, I'd like to write a new beginning of the Bible. No snakes. No scary things at all.'

'I'm sure it would be a very interesting story, Evie, but it would not be, err, the same.'

'You're right there, Miss. I wouldn't have any of those nude people eating apples. You don't have to take your clothes off to eat an apple. It's daft!'

'Evie, you've strayed into Religious Education lessons now. That isn't the sex education lesson.'

'Well, my mum says no one in a primary school wants sex, Miss. Arjun doesn't, do you, Arjun? See Miss, he doesn't.'

'But Evie, Arjun did not say anything.'

'He doesn't have to – it's obvious.'

'Well, that's quite enough, Evie. I don't want to hear any more about sex, err, I mean sex education. It's not appropriate now.'

'Why not, Miss?'

'Because this is the *Music* lesson! And I have to teach you all a song for the end-of-term concert and it's got nothing to do with sex education.'

'What's the song, Miss?'

'It's – oh dear! I've quite forgotten. It's "Rock-a-bye baby".'

Evie thrust her hands on her hips. 'Well! My mum says that is a cruel song, Miss. She never sings it.'

'Well, I —'

'Stringing a baby up a tree isn't right. And in the wind an'all. Definitely not right.'

'I don't think the song means quite —'

'Would you do it, Miss? Fasten your baby up a tree in its cradle? I bet you wouldn't. You're too kind. And you'd have to buy a new cradle to replace the broken one, an' all. Have you thought of that?'

'Oh dear. Since you feel so strongly about it perhaps we had better change it. How about "Ring a ring o' roses"?'

'Miss! We can't sing that! My mum says it is about children falling down dead of fever! We couldn't sing it because it's 'orrible and we would all be crying, and we wouldn't get to sleep at night!'

'Evie, It doesn't necessarily mean —'

'I'm beginning to cry already, Miss.'

'Oh dear, Evie. Well, have you got any suggestions of your own?'

Graham now piped up.

'Miss! Let's all sing "Three Blind Mice"!'

'We can all yell our heads off, and run up and down on the spot, and make cutting actions! Great!'

A scream came from Evie.

'How could you agree to that, Miss? It's terrible! Ugh! I'll tell my mum, Miss. She won't like it. Not one bit! You'll be for it!'

'Evie! I haven't agreed to it, and I'm not going to! CLASS! Get ready to sing "Twinkle, twinkle". You all know it.'

'Oh no! Not again!' moaned the class all together.

Evie's hands were once again on her hips.

'That song is out-of-date, Miss. It says "how I wonder what you are", and my mum says we know what stars are now. We should NOT be singing out-of-date songs. It's not right!'

By now, Miss was beginning to harbour uncharitable thoughts about Evie's mother. She threw her arms up.

'Okay! Okay! You don't like my choices so here's what we are going to do. Get yourselves into groups of four (sounds of scraping chairs and animated chatter). No, Stella, FOUR. I don't care that you've got five friends – I said FOUR. Now, write down on the paper in front of you the name of one song you would like us all to sing. Robin, you do not do that with a pencil, it's not nice! Abigail, that's Anil's chair; he got there first. Yes he did, because I say so, dear, so just let go. Then you must all discuss your choice and decide which one the group round the table likes best okay? Then we'll get the whole class to vote for the class song. Right, off you go. I'll come round and answer any of your questions eventually.'

Miss sauntered from table to table listening to the arguments amid raised voices. Behind her she could hear a high-pitched orator starting 'My mum says —' before being interrupted by a deeper tone from one of the boys: 'Well, my dad says different, our Evie, and he's bigger than your mum.'

Miss smiled contentedly at the success of her strategy. They don't teach you that at college!

An Educated Guess

It is natural for parents to want to show that they are interested in their children's schooling, and none more so than teacher parents. This little gem was told by Marcus Brampton to his pals in The Babbling Brook about a colleague who arrived one morning chuckling to himself, so much so that all his senior management team colleagues refused to start the early morning meeting until he had shared his good cheer with them. As always, personal anecdotes like this are inevitably better coming from the mouth of the author, especially one that can hardly get the story out because of the tears in his eyes.

You will appreciate that like most teacher parents, I suspect I can't let any opportunity go by without using it to 'educate' my seven-year old daughter.

It was like this. Two days ago I foolishly asked Tirzah to estimate how many peas there were in a packet of frozen ones my wife had brought home from the Co-op. I thought it might be 'educational' to verify the accuracy of her estimate by getting her to take out ten peas, weigh them and then calculate how many would fit into the 500g pack. Tirzah had her own idea. 'No, Dad, that's not good enough. I've done the estimate – you must now count the whole lot to get the exact amount. It's only fair!' She then flounced out to go and play with her pals.

I did start counting the peas, partly as a matter of honour and partly because I wanted to know the answer, but I never completed the task. Not only did the peas keep rolling off the table, but when my wife came into the kitchen and saw what I was doing, she screamed, 'What on earth are you doing with the peas for tonight's dinner party!' This setback did not hold me back in my quest for opportunities to practise 'education' on our daughter. Tea-time last night was as usual the moment for the inevitable parent question:

'So, what did you do at school today, then?'

As usual too Tirzah's eyes went up and she sighed. She placed her elbows firmly on the table, leaving knife and fork pointing skyward. She considered the question carefully as though she had never heard it before. Wife and I paused in our munching and looked at her. We need not have worried. It was the normal moment's thought, and we duly got the answer we fully expected.

'Nothing, Daddy. Just school.'

She then resumed her attack on her fish fingers, leaving us the usual opening for follow-up questions. We were surprised, therefore, when Tirzah put her knife and fork down halfway through a chip and turned to look straight at me.

'Do you know what, Daddy, we had a new girl arrive in the class today and she's a coloured girl but she speaks really good English. She's ever so nice.'

My wife joined in. 'Oh, good. So where does she come from then?'

'She's from India,' replied Tirzah, showing some awe in her voice.

My teacher-parenthood took hold of me at this point. 'That's good, really nice. And where is India then?' I could at last spy a use for the spinning globe in the corner, the one I had purchased at the PTA sale.

Tirzah paused with her fork halfway to her mouth. She laid it down and thought hard. Finally, she put her head in cupped hands in front of her, leaning on the table.

'Well, Dad, I don't know exactly where it is, but it can't be far because she goes home for lunch.'

The Meaning of Words

I've said it before and I'll say it again, said Marcus: the English language is a wondrous creation. No one knows any longer what is the real English – not even the English. It is such a global treasure that every country seems to create new idioms and new words on a seemingly daily basis. Such new words and phrases provide twists and turns so that people of my age (a venerable but unspecified age) feel like strangers in our own tongue.

Bear in mind, there was a time when 'cool' meant 'not hot', when a 'queen' wore a crown and sat on a throne, when we used to mow 'grass' and cook from a 'pot', and when the British claimed exclusive right to a 'flat' meaning an apartment, a 'boot' was where you kept the luggage in your car, and 'sidewalks' simply did not exist. And as for the language of rap, well, it is rich and colourful in a way that inspires its devotees but leaves the rest of us bothered and bewildered.

Our problem or perhaps our 'comfort' is that we do not have an Academy to determine matters of language and taste as the French have. There is no control. The English language can mean what anyone wants it to mean and can find others to understand.

And it is not just young people's inventions. Some common and extensive uses of the English language have evolved slowly and naturally from the languages used in politics, law, business, sport and music. And rather delightfully, some equally widely used words and phrases are left-overs from a bygone age.

My wife and I were in New Delhi when, during the night, an earthquake rocked northern India. Delhi was on the edge, but the shocks were still strong and the aftershocks frightening because they were unexpected. Our hotel room swayed from side to side; the bed rocked around; our suitcases slid across the floor. After the usual bewilderment and daft question, 'What is it?' my wife and I leapt out of bed and rushed out into the street. Everything quietened down after a couple of hours and we returned to our room not to sleep, but to sip tea with other guests who had become instant friends and allies.

What has this to do with the development of the English language? Well, next morning the *Hindustan Times* carried the full story of course, and in the front-page description was a sentence that has stuck with me ever since: 'Denizens rushed from their abodes.' What a truly precise and memorable expression, straight out of the Victorian era, but this was the 1990s.

So, in my view we are better off without an Academy. The English language has proved itself capable of absorbing just about anything – which brings me to my little tale of Dai and his Dai-isms.

*****

In English lessons secondary school pupils will usually come across malapropisms. It would be sad if they didn't. It is the name given to the use of an incorrect word in place of one with a similar pronunciation. A well-known one is 'dancing a flamingo' instead of 'dancing a flamenco'. Malapropism comes from the character of Mrs Malaprop in the eighteenth-century play *The Rivals* by Richard Brinsley Sheridan. Mrs Malaprop uses nonsense phrases throughout the play: for example, '*illiterate* him quite from your memory' (instead of 'obliterate'), and 'she's as headstrong as an *allegory* on the banks of the Nile' (instead of 'alligator').

Pupils are also likely to be told about spoonerisms, where letters in two words in a phrase are transposed with comic repercussions, such as 'the town drain went through the station,' instead of 'the down train went through the station,' or 'fighting a liar.' instead of 'lighting a fire,' and 'nosey little cook,' instead of cosy little nook'. This aberration was reputedly first perpetrated by Dr William Spooner, a Fellow of an Oxford college.

But few will have come across 'Dai-isms'. They are worth knowing, and their provenance is a sign of the multilingual and multicultural country we live in. This is how they came about.

My good friend Dai (that narrows it down to a few hundred thousand men and boys) from North Wales was brought up in a Welsh-speaking family and did not learn English until he went to secondary school at the age of eleven. He had hardly mastered the skill when I met him at university.

Apart from other lovable linguistic characteristics Dai had an enormous, even impossible, problem with English proverbs which, he assured me, were very different from Welsh ones. His Welsh heritage of colourful language drove him to try his hand at similar English flowery gestures. So, he graduated naturally to using proverbs and well-known sayings. Unfortunately, he had no idea what they meant or in most cases what they actually were. They became muddled in his mind and mixed up in his speech. But that did not stop him regaling us all with his proverbial metatheses.

Dai-isms became legendary as we traversed the labyrinth of university life together. The first one that threw me (and not only me) was 'I've got a bone to grind with you.' It was the sort of statement that rang true, and it was only after our conversation had proceeded that I suddenly realised it was not quite right! Nor was the expression, 'If he does not watch it, he'll smile on the other foot,' although you must surely admit that it has an ominous ring.

This was also what happened with 'Let lying dogs sleep,' and 'Many hands spoil light broth.' They are not right but you have a sneaking feeling that they ought to be. 'No thanks, I have had a dearth of it,' foxed us all for a while, until it dawned on us that he had got completely the opposite meaning for 'dearth'. He was quite convinced it meant 'plenty' or 'a good sufficiency', rather than a lack of it. It did not matter until he was at dinner with the Senior Tutor and his wife. The Senior Tutor, a benign and well-meaning scholar asked, on behalf of his charming wife, whether Dai had enjoyed the meal.

While the wife, a perfect hostess, looked on with self-satisfied smile, Dai replied in robust undergraduate style: 'You didn't half give me a dearth of food. Most memorable.' The Senior Tutor's wife had to go and lie down much to Dai's puzzlement. It was eventually all sorted out, of course, and led to a learned discourse on the development of language but Dai still could not get out of the habit of using the expression. 'I realise now that I was treading on hot potatoes but it's such a nice word,' he would protest, 'and conveys just what I mean. It's not really my fault if the meaning has changed.'

But one can get used to anything, so I was ready when he assailed me with 'I've got an axe to pick with you.' 'Axe' and 'pick' in the same phrase could have thrown anyone! However, my ear was attuned by then. I could take his subsequent 'picking' in my stride.

Even so, I was both taken aback and full of admiration at his longest, most telling, and most fluent proverbial misapplication, which tripped off his tongue when complaining of a fellow student's inability to see the right answer even when the solution was staring him in the face. Dai shook his head in anguished disappointment, and with a great sigh said: 'Well, you can take Muhammad to the mountain, but you can't make him drink.' True enough, but not correct!

The whole notion of playing around with proverbs appealed to me and I introduced it to many groups of my English students over the next forty years. They relished trying their own hand at it – too much so in some cases. They just mutilated rather than enhanced the English language. But that's students for you. 'Give them a penny and they will sell it for a pound.'

Many came up with variations on 'A bird in hand is worth two in the bush' and 'Birds of a feather flock together'. And I will never forget the fourteen-year old, who eventually became a high-ranking civil servant, catching me out with a quotation from Shakespeare, and adding with the most benign of grins: 'The smile is on the other foot, now, Sir.'

In my notes from those days I have found a number of them, such as 'When birds of a feather flock together they spoil the bush,' and 'Birds flocking in your bush eat your berries.' A bit pedestrian, but at least they were having a go. More exotic and original were 'A barking dog never bites his best friend,' and 'A bit of what you fancy is the root of all evil.'

But I really appreciated the poetic 'A nod is as good as a wink to a blind horse,' and the aphoristic wit of 'Drop your shorts and lift their spirits.' There is not much you can add after that!

The Things Kids Say

A friend told the cautionary tale of classroom banter that teachers will be only too aware of – the ease with which kids can cut in with a question or observation that utterly throws you or sends you off in the wrong direction. You, the teacher, have to think adroitly on your feet and reply with gentle understanding of how important the question must be to the questioner. And then, in another kind of classroom encounter you can jump to conclusions, wrong ones, when kids simply say the first thing that comes into their heads, they knowing absolutely precisely what they are getting at and you totally surprised and mystified. Handle such a situation wrongly and the child can get really annoyed about the teacher's apparent obtuseness in not being able to comprehend the issue. Let me illustrate this, said Marcus Brampton, with this story about my wife Ros's encounters with one young lad, Rory, of Year 8.

Young people, as I am sure you know, often have only a hazy idea about comparative ages. Well, my wife occasionally taught part-time in my school. As it happens, she has white hair and I do not. Nonetheless she is some years younger than me. She had been standing in for an absent colleague for some weeks teaching Chemistry. Then at the start of one lesson one small twelve-year-old, Rory, puzzled by her white hair and the same surname as the Headmaster with his shock of brown hair, could contain himself no longer.

'Are you the Headmaster's mother, Miss?'

Luckily my wife has a sense of humour! And being both a good scientist and a good teacher she seized the opportunity for a lesson on keratin filament. Situation saved, pupil more knowledgeable: an excellent outcome, except to my wife's ego but we won't go into that.

She also had to think on her feet when she was standing in for an absent colleague and was teaching a Religious Education lesson. She was involved in a discussion with the same Year 8 group about their experience of bereavement, if any. The conversation got around to parents, grandparents and relatives. During the animated discussion up popped Rory again. He had been sitting silent and thoughtful at the front. Suddenly he shot his hand into the air,

'Miss, Miss, you should know. My mother's on the TV, Miss.'

That could have stopped the lesson in its tracks. But being an RE lesson my wife knew that all kinds of interventions could occur. It paid to be tolerant.

'That's interesting, Rory, but where your mum works is not really relevant to this lesson, is it?'

'Yes it is, Miss. It's very relevant to bereavement.'

Knowing the boy's humble background, my wife looked dubious. 'Hmm, how on earth can it be relevant to bereavement, Rory? Perhaps she'd like to be on TV, is that it?'

'No, Miss, that's not right. She really is on the telly!'

My wife could sense a rumbling round the class. Some of the others were looking at each other. She thought she had better cut this short. 'OK that's enough now.'

At this there was a chorus of shouting, protesting voices: 'It's true, Miss! Listen to him, Miss. His mother really is on the telly – you should believe us kids when we tell you summat important.'

'All right, all right. Well, you, Susie, tell me why it is important to know that Rory's mother is on the TV?'

'Because, Miss, she's right on top of the TV. She's dead, you see, Miss, and her ashes are in an urn on top of Rory's and his dad's TV set. Everybody knows that!'

Well, my wife didn't but she does now. She now makes a point of believing *everything* children say until proved wrong!

Little Rory was deeper into the significance of that RE lesson than anyone, including my wife, could ever imagine.

When your power and influence as a teacher is suddenly brought home to you it can be an awesome and sobering experience. You suddenly realise that you are not just a lecturer out at the front but a force, a guiding spirit in loco parentis. You will always be there for them, you will be 'Miss who knows everything', and 'Sir who feels for you', the teacher who 'suffers everything with you'.

Winning without Knowing

In my experience, said Marcus, all sixth formers are innately, or constitutionally, or simply by inclination, iconoclasts, saboteurs, revolutionaries. Well, if they are not so inclined in the sixth form or the first year in higher education when *are* they going to be? And I say 'they', and not 'we' because, if my memory serves me right, we 'post-1944 Education Act grammar school pupils' were models of sobriety and correctness. That is the considered view of an octogenarian who prefers to see all behaviour in the light of 'when I was young we did that or did not do that.' It is a comfortable way of looking at life. Blame the young and pour another gin.

But sixth formers can in fact set the whole tone of the school and can seal the school's role as a place of entertainment as well as education – indeed the two words are surely interchangeable! I consider myself to be fortunate to have studied only in a Sixth Form with 'characters' and only taught in schools with teenagers with what are called 'high spirits'.

At my first school as a teacher an all-boys school and in my first term no less, I became the unwitting participant in one of the sixth formers' 'humorous' activities. I was not alone – all the staff took part. The difference was that they had an inkling that they were central characters but could not work out why while I, the new boy, neither knew why nor that I was even a pawn in the game.

It was a game designed by a small coterie of ingenious prefects but involving all sixty of the Upper Sixth. It was motivated, I was later told, by the urgent need to 'ward off morning assembly boredom', and at a higher level to 'give some meaning to life'. Only a sardonic sixth former could come up with that explanation. What happened was this.

Towards the end of the Autumn term, my first term as I said, I was conscious of a ripple of excitement at the back of Big

School, which is what the school assembly hall was called, whenever myself and a couple of other staff, including my English Department colleague Simon, climbed onto the stage to sit in the staff seats, traditionally behind the Head. He controlled assembly from his carved oak high-back chair behind the ancient table at the front of the stage. I noticed, but thought little about, the puzzling murmuring that only involved the back of the assembly stalls until the very last assembly of the term.

As I bounded up the steps onto the back of the stage with my habitual jauntiness, I was suddenly conscious not of a ripple of muted sound, but an audible, if slightly sotto voce, cheer. It was so marked that the urchins in the front rows were moved to turn round and gawp. Mr MacTavish, the Deputy Head, called grandly the Second Master, was moved to stalk between the rows, brow furrowed and academic gown whirling. The murmuring subsided.

I thought no more about it as I, along with forty staff and a handful of boys, bellowed out the Christmas hymn. It was only after the assembly that the Head Boy approached me in the corridor on my way back to my classroom and spilt the beans.

'Excuse me, Sir, you may not be aware of this but we – the prefects that is – have been running our usual betting book. The staff are, err, the horses Sir, and because you were new you were at long odds but you won. Congratulations.'

'I did what?! Win what?'

'Well sometimes the betting is on who will appear at morning assembly most often in the Autumn Term or it could be which member of staff actually sings the morning hymn. But this year, sir, the betting was on which member of staff wore the most varied ties during the term, and which wore the loudest ties. You, Sir, have won both categories hands down!'

It was true that I had a large number of college, club, regimental and flashy patterned ties and it pleased me to ring the changes daily. It seems that I had qualified for the shortlist in the competition, which was played out in the last few assemblies of the term, and that my interchanging batch of Christmas ties with Santas and Christmas trees and sledges and snowmen, had won the day.

'Your two sixth form backers, sir, have swept the board but I cannot, of course, divulge their names. You share both prizes, that is, £5 each, so here is a tenner .' And with that he produced a ten-pound note – a currency I had never held before in my life. You should be aware that the monthly take-home pay of a teacher in 1961 was only some £40, ie about £10 a week, so I was truly gobsmacked. The Head Boy thrust the note into my hand and disappeared.

I stood totally at a loss holding this extraordinary token of success. I suppose thoughts about how it might be spent were going through my mind, but my reverie was disturbed by a discreet cough at my back. I turned. It was Mr MacTavish, the Second Master.

'Naughty, naughty,' he said, wagging his finger and then holding out his hand. 'Give it to me before you get too attached to it,' he added. 'There is no way that this school will tolerate the encouragement of betting. I will deal with it and make sure in future you do not get involved with such dreadful goings-on. Dear me, dear me!'

'But I didn't know I had participated in this competition. How am I going to know and what are you going to do with my, err, the £10?' I yelled after him but he had gone. I heard a chuckle behind me. It was Perky Perkins from the Maths Department, a lovable rogue if there was ever one.

'Not quick enough,' he sighed. 'But you'll get smarter. Don't worry, old MacTavish will put it in the school charity. He always does.'

'You mean he always knows who wins?'

'Not always but mostly. He hasn't got me this year and I've just won the Lower Sixth prize for not wearing my gown on stage at Assembly more times than anyone else – third time in four years. Got my fiver here.' He produced a crisp note out of his top pocket and brandished it at me. 'I shall, of course, be putting it into the school funds, via a few buns at the tuck shop of course!'

'Don't put yourself to that trouble, Perkins. I will gladly enhance school funds for you.'

Perky wheeled round. MacTavish was standing in the office door next to us. With one accurate sweep of his arm, he dispossessed Perky of his precious note. 'I know how despicable you think gambling and betting are, Mr Perkins. Very commendable. I shall let the Head know of both your generous gestures.' And once again Big Mac flounced off down the corridor.

The competitions were ritually banned again the following year and ritually resurrected. But what the prizes were I know not – I never won one again.

Rising Standards

When Marcus Brampton got the job of Headmaster at Market Upabit, the time came for he and his wife to go house-hunting. The young estate agent was keen for them to view a particular 'very attractive piece of land, half an acre of it, prime stuff, much sought after and in the next village to the town – a must see,' he reckoned. And so they did and as they got out of the car it looked every bit as attractive as the young chap had described it.

'Follow me,' he said then set off on a brisk walk across the top of the field. It sloped ever so slightly towards a brook along the bottom with a dividing hedge alongside.

'Wonderful location,' he cried over his shoulder. 'A snip at the price. Lots you can do with it, OK? Shall we move on to the next property?'

'Er, just a minute what's the hurry? I'd like to walk round the plot a bit more with my wife, if that's all right?' Marcus put up a restraining hand.

The agent was about to reply when a huge roar split the air, making both Marcus and wife start, whirl round and stare at the hedge at the bottom of the field.

'Good Lor'. What on earth was that?'

The agent took it in his stride. 'Nothing to worry about.' But before their leader could continue, Mrs Brampton pointed at the hedge, eyes opened wide.

'Look there.'

And there, over the hedge, a long, grey trunk swung lazily in the air and a pair of grey, flapping ears flopped over the hedge top. Two eyes peered at them twenty feet away.

'Ah yes,' said the estate agent, 'I was about to mention that. That's the winter quarters of a major international circus. Exciting isn't it ? Lots of interest for your little kids.'

Another roar rose up from across the field – not an elephant-like sound.

'You mean if they aren't eaten!' Mrs Brampton had in mind Stanley Holloway's monologue, 'Albert and the Lion'. 'I don't think this is quite what we are looking for. We'll go and have a look at the next plot!'

The Bramptons did not become circus neighbours. But the school and the circus built up a very fruitful arrangement. Sons and daughters of tumblers, tightrope walkers, lion tamers and clowns spent winter months at the school and the feeder schools; the circus used the school hall for some training and, 'my goodness,' said Marcus, 'didn't our standard of PE rocket! The influence of the circus children rubbed off with the locals. Before long we had students taking part in national gymnastic and trampoline competitions, and more kids than ever wanting to stay for after-school gym clubs. Bronwen, the daughter of the high wire trapeze duo, a lovely, bright teenager, would make her way down the corridors via cartwheels, front flips and back flips wonderful to encounter, a tonic for the day. Imagine having that talent in abundance on hand! It affected one student so much that, although on leaving school at fifteen he became a 'turkey-sexer' (really) at a local turkey farm, he gave it up, joined the circus and became a ringmaster. I don't think any careers adviser would think of recommending that route to a teenager '

Marcus was proud of the relationship of school and circus, but it was not to last. The government decided to fund travelling teachers for travelling folk, and so circus children got their education all the year round on their travels. That is how it should be. Right for the circus, but sad for Marcus and Market Upabit School.

But they did not leave without making a lasting impression on all who had the privilege of being in school with them. And many Upabit parents will remember them, too. In the early spring, just before the circus packed up for its summer tour, Marcus Brampton organised the usual Parents Evening for parents of existing students and parents of pupils from the feeder schools. It involved a showcase for the school's music, dance and gymnastics provided by the school students with the help of some staff. The audience of parents and grandparents sat in a wide square round the central acting space.

Following the music and dance, at the end of a gymnastics display impressive like no other, the Head of PE invited parents to take part in 'a few, easy gymnastic moves'. No one moved A few looked enquiringly at each other. Then two fathers put their hands up and took their coats off, and then another one from the opposite corner. For a few moments the three tumbled on mats with some of the school students and staff. The audience of parents applauded with sympathy and laughter.

'Good show.'

'Well done!'

Then one of the tumbling parents indicated to another to get onto his shoulders. He did, swinging himself up and letting go of any supporting hands. The audience gasped and gaped, hands poised apart, eyes following every move, as the third parent said, 'I'll have a go at that,' and immediately swung himself on top of the second one's shoulders. Before the parents could gasp more and continue the applause, three more parents got up out of the audience and made the pyramid even bigger, and then two more, and finally one of the students let out a yell, did a series of cartwheels and clambered right to the top. And if that was not astonishing enough for the country town parent audience, the whole pyramid suddenly collapsed and nine tumblers bounced and rolled right up to the feet of the front row.

Marcus stood, leading the enthusiastic applause and grateful thanks. The Haranni Troupe had done the school proud.

But that was not the end. Marcus beckoned an elderly 'grandad' forward. There was another short gasp as all the locals knew who it was: Compo the Clown, one of the most famous 'Auguste' clowns, those comic characters who act as the foil to the white-faced clowns – a tradition of slapstick comedy, with light and dark humour that characterises circus and pantomime entertainment. He was already well known to most of the kids because of his road safety work in primary schools. This was his first, and sadly his last, appearance at the 'big school'. He was not far from the end of his life, but his charisma, his aura, his just being there, was magnetic. He was not in clown character, not intent on making comedy, just radiating warmth – a warmth and humour that is captured on his headstone in the village church. Marcus did not mean it as a grand gesture, but grand it was. Oh no it wasn't! Oh yes it was!

A Good Job

It may seem odd, but some students can be just too good, too friendly, too anxious to please. They can cause distress, even despair, simply because you fear on their behalf threats that they do not begin to imagine. Hence, they can be prone to pranks, to exploitation, to bullying, but not care about it. It is you, the teacher, the mentor, the guardian who cares. They will sail blithely through life's vicissitudes unaware of the panic in their wake. They are not irritating – that's a negative feeling – they are more, shall we say, anxiety-inducing. You just want them to be safe, cared for, happy. And teachers worth their salt will strive to do just that.

One such student Marcus Brampton remembered with great affection. He had never encountered a young person so determined to be helpful to parents, relations, teachers, school secretary, lab assistants, caretaker bus drivers, in fact everyone he came into contact with – so much so that it made all of those charged with teaching and caring for him very nervous when they saw him coming.

He was lovely but trouble travelled in his wake. His teachers knew just about how to handle the social dangers that his approach to life engendered. People who did not know him or anyone like him could be in for a surprise.

George was doing work experience at a local hotel. Marcus made sure the Head of Special Educational Needs had briefed the manager on George's autistic tendencies (which at that time were not so well understood as now – in fact not understood at all by many teachers.)

On his first morning, Courtney Hilton, the manager, told George he could start by simply hoovering the conference room carpet ready for an afternoon meeting. The manager watched him for a while and satisfied that all was going well, left the room. Then due to pressure of work he forgot all about George until lunchtime. When he returned to the conference room three hours later, he found George still hoovering the carpet which is, after all, what he had been told to do. The carpet was by now extremely clean – indeed it had never been so shiny – but totally threadbare through to the floor in the centre. The manager blanched, gulped and, with great presence of mind, turned off the power, thus curtailing further activity.

'Jolly good, George.'

'Oh, thank you, Sir.'

'It's, er, really clean, isn't it?'

'It certainly is, Sir. I had some trouble with the curly patterns but no dust here now, Sir. Have you got any more carpets you want hoovering? I'm quite into it now.'

'No, no that's all the cleaning we need. I suggest you go …'.In truth Courtney Hilton had no idea at all what he was going to do. He could not countenance any more threadbare carpets, and no immediate thought came into his whirring brain at that moment. He seriously considered sending George back to school but decided that it would be devastating for the lad, and for him too. He wanted the boy to succeed – but at what price?

George needed supervision, that was for sure. The kitchen! That's the place. A word to chef Pierre and George would be watched with a hawk's eye. Pierre scrutinised every move in his kitchen. Oodles of washing up to be done, lots of fetching and carrying and stocking shelves. He was sure that Pierre was the man. George would be safe there and so would the hotel.

So, off he went.

On his way to the kitchen George, who was wearing the hotel's distinctive white shirt and black waistcoat, passed through the dining room where two senior executives from the hotel chain Head Office were having lunch. Although no direct announcement was made, Courtney knew they were doing their annual inspection of luncheon service.

One of the executives spied George and hailed him. 'Excuse me. Could you get us some more bread?'

'Certainly, Sir,' replied George, very proud to be of service. He bowed, which was immediately impressive and strode off through the kitchen door. Moments later Manager Hilton arrived at the main dining room, full of good cheer, all thoughts of threadbare carpets now banished. Mrs Duerden, the housekeeper, had assured him that she had been waiting months for an excuse to get a new carpet for the meeting room. Mrs Duerden was ecstatic so Manager Hilton was now in seventh heaven.

Just as Mr Hilton came through the door, George was emerging from the kitchen through the swing doors that divided kitchen and dining room and was bearing down on the executives' table. Fine – the decision seemed to be working. But then Courtney did a double-take and stopped abruptly in his tracks. On the plate George was holding poised at shoulder height in true waiter fashion, was a single loaf, a one metre-long square catering loaf, the sort restaurants use to slice rounds of bread for toast or to crumble for bread-crumbs. Courtney stood agog.

George had been asked to provide bread and bread he would provide.

All the manager could do was watch George approach the executives' table with a smile. He continued to stand, mouth open and mind again whirling, transfixed by the scene unfolding before him. Then in a burst of enlightened frenzy he rushed to the table just as George was presenting the loaf.

'Gentlemen!' cried the manager, interposing himself between loaf and guests. 'Let me explain We thought you might like to see how fresh our bread is. George has kindly brought it for us. Now would you like to sample a crusty piece or a slice from the centre?'

'Well, that's very novel and very thoughtful of you,' said the senior man. 'Never given much thought to the uses of catering loaves before. Well done.'

'And well done to you, young man,' he added to George. George bowed again.

And so George got an accolade from the representatives of Head Office, and then a cash bonus, a crisp £20 note, from the hotel manager – a classic example of not just damage limitation but damage aversion! Everyone was happy. In management-speak, it had turned out to be a 'win-win situation'.

A few years later when George had left school and had undergone a series of therapies that were at the cutting edge at the time, Marcus met him in town and in the course of their conversation Marcus asked if he remembered the success of his work experience.

'I've always remembered it Sir,' he said. 'At the time I couldn't understand what all the fuss was about. Why on earth I should get a cash bonus for just doing the job. I was asked to get more bread and that is what I did. If they only wanted slices or rolls they should have said so. But it is nice to know that employers can be so generous. That's what I think was so special about the event.'

As Marcus shook hands with him and wished him well, George stopped him. 'I am sure you would like to know that I framed the £20 note. It reminds me of how thoughtful employers can be.'

Nine Pupils Shot

Marcus Brampton was quietly going about his head-magisterial duties, interviewing a professional couple, a solicitor and his accountant wife. They were considering sending their eldest son to this new school, which promised so much, or to the nearby public school which had achieved so much. They were getting along nicely when in through the door burst a breathless youngster, quivering with excitement.

'Sir! Sir!' Then a gulp. 'Sir, Elsie McCreadie's been shot!'

Stunned silence. Parents' jaws sagged. 'What sort of school is this?' Marcus would have been surprised if that hadn't flashed through their minds! Meanwhile he was busy composing himself.

None of his pre-headship training, nor previous experience, could be brought to bear easily on this singular situation. But thanks to his experience of leading soldiers in the Territorial Army, he kept his presence of mind.

'Really?' he commented in a languid tone, suggestive of easy, effective, experienced management of a trifling day-to-day issue. 'I'll tell you what, go and tell the Deputy.'

He smiled at the breathless young girl and at his own instant ingenuity. He swivelled back imperiously to the two ashen parents. 'Do excuse me for a moment,' he said smoothly retaining the comforting smile. 'There has obviously been a bit of an accident. Do excuse me. I won't be long. My secretary will bring you a cup of tea.'

Without waiting for an answer, he swept out, calling Angie for tea before dashing across the sports field where he could spy a knot of staff and students gathering by the boundary hedge. The crowd parted for him so that he could survey the scene. Elsie was certainly injured. She was rubbing her cheek and mouthing what might have been obscenities. As well as Elie, it seemed that eight other students had also been injured, all of them either sitting or standing under the hedge, tended by staff first aiders. There appeared to be another group of people on the other side of the hedge.

A cyclone of thoughts swirled round in Marcus's head. His eyes darted from one person to another and finally fixed on his Assistant Head, Oliver bending over Elsie McCreadie whose obscenities increased in volume and extent as the first aiders applied Dettol and plasters.

'What on earth is going on, Ollie? It looks like the siege of Sebastopol!'

Ollie was a dour, unspectacular Yorkshireman, never flustered, always reassuring.

SC
21

'Nothing to worry about much Headmaster. Quite simple really, though not something they teach you at university It seems that a pheasant-shooting party was crossing the field on the other side of the school boundary hedge. Those gentlemen over there.' He waved a hand at the tweed clad, rather forlorn group clustered round the other side of the hedge. 'It seems that they were proceeding in a regulation straight line with regulatory intervals between guns and a keen sense of excitement – well, that's what His Lordship's gamekeeper Maltravers there tells me.' Oliver rubbed his nose contemplatively. 'Left-hand Charlie, one of the paying "guns" appears to be a bit of an amateur at game-shooting. He heard a rustling in the bushes and without thinking, he let off one of his barrels in the general direction of the bushes here.'

'Good Lord, how utterly stupid,' said Marcus. 'And what a terrible coincidence that our kids were passing along the hedge.'

'Er not so much of a coincidence, Headmaster. They were the cause of the rustling noise, you see.'

'Rustling noise? How did they make a "rustling" noise?'

'Hmm best not go into much detail just here, Headmaster. The fact is that as well as doing that they were also smoking – eight smokers, one box of matches and one look-out, Elsie's little brother, Cyrus.'

'Not a very good look-out, then.'

'No, not at all. Seems he was smoking, too, further along the hedge.'

Marcus turned to the senior first aider.

'I take it they're all OK, Sally?'

'Well, as right as anyone can be when they have been peppered with full-bore shot. But only superficial injuries. Only poor old Elsie seems to have a piece of shot embedded in her cheek. I am taking her off to Fenborough Hospital now.'

Marcus turned to Elsie who was holding her cheek. 'Well, Elsie, that's a rather extreme punishment for smoking, isn't it?'

'Not what you would expect, Sir. It's usually an effing detention. I hope it doesn't become regular.'

'Well, it won't if you stop smoking, Elsie.'

'Hm! I'll try, Sir. That I will.'

'In that case, I'll just keep shooting as a back-up punishment, Elsie. Now off you go with Miss Blount and get yourself put right. I'll get in touch with your mum and dad.'

He watched teacher and student trudge across the field.

'Not much gets Elsie down, Olly.'

'You are right there, nothing short of two barrels of shot!'

'Hey there!' A voice hailed them from the other side of the hedge. It was My Lord's gamekeeper.

'Is it all sorted now? We need to crack on.'

Marcus knew he had to restrain himself. His Lordship was a powerful force. Marcus eyed the gamekeeper. The gamekeeper glared back.

'You have just shot nine of my pupils, Sir,' said Marcus very deliberately.

'It's all right,' came the breezy answer. 'We're insured!'

Marcus spluttered. He could hardly believe his ears. 'That's not quite the point, is it? Some idiot could have committed a crime or at least a serious piece of negligence. Don't you think some apology is needed for your thoughtlessness? I expect His Lordship will be hearing from the kids' parents, or the police, in due course.'

'I say, that's a bit heavy, Headmaster. I didn't expect that type of attitude.' With that he wheeled away and led his posse across the field to the far woods.

Marcus stood watching them. He was speechless. Ollie sidled up to him. 'I shouldn't take it too badly, Marcus. You'll get used to the ways of the country in time. Neither the police nor Elsie's dad will press charges, you know.'

'But they must, it's terrible, more than just negligence, it's gross negligence. They have to do something to bring some consideration of others into it.'

Ollie was right. A sergeant called on Marcus a day or two later. A 'courtesy call', he explained. The Super wanted Marcus to know that he had reprimanded the gamekeeper, who had taken the admonishment 'very gracefully'. 'No need for His Lordship to be bothered with it d'you see? And, by the way, Elsie's dad doesn't want any further action, either. He works on the estate, you see, and His Lordship's insurers will see him okay. Best not to interfere Sir, right? So I'll be off now. Thank you for seeing me. I'll tell the Super everything is fine. Good morning.' The policeman saluted and turned on his heel before Marcus could gather his breath.

Marcus just sat there. Ollie popped his head round the door. 'Okay Headmaster? There really is nothing you can do, or ought to do. This community is older and stronger than you and me – you'll come to appreciate its funny, err, "traditions" eventually!'

Marcus sat for a long time tapping his fingers together. Finally he snapped out of his reverie and smiled to himself. 'I don't suppose I would feel half as bad about it if the solicitor and his accountant wife had stayed. They didn't even wait for the tea!'

There is a sequel to this episode – a tale of rural deprivation …

Rural Deprivation

It was barely a month after the infamous shooting incident when, you will remember, young Elsie had been inadvertently shot by a member of his Lordship's pheasant shoot, while snatching a quick fag behind the school hedge along with eight of her classmates. Headmaster Marcus Brampton was attending an education conference in London organised by his Headteachers' association. The general theme of the conference centred on the perceived slow progress of support for the large number of secondary schools now popping up all over the country as the post-war baby boom moved inexorably on.

Marcus was becoming increasingly irritated by speaker after speaker berating the government's lack of action in the inner cities, preferring, one speaker pronounced with red-faced anger, those havens of peaceful tranquillity, those two-hundred-year-old throwbacks to a Constable-like serenity, those calm and comfortable rural areas, so beloved by this country's right wing! Marcus, in the body of the hall, could contain himself no longer. From his seat he shouted out, 'Rural schools have problems, too! I bet you've never had nine of your pupils shot!'

That stopped the speaker in his tracks! It also stopped everything else. The speaker gawped. The Chairman scanned the large auditorium to trace the intruder. Press photographers stood to get a better shot of what promised to be the picture of the day. His pals on either side of him shuffled their chairs sideways. The rest of the audience looked around, or stood, or talked excitedly amongst themselves.

The Chair finally got a grip. He leaned forward, took command of the microphone and in the same action motioned the guest speaker to take his seat, with just a hurried whispered conversation. The Chair cleared his throat, 'Ladies and gentlemen, it is highly unusual for a member of this

Association to interrupt a speaker. Our guest will now continue and I am sure you will give him the applause he deserves.'

Some applause broke out, light and tentative but most of the audience were still trying to identify who it was who was livening up the conference more than somewhat – who had offered the possibility of dispelling their growing boredom with the succession of anti-government speeches delivered in the same ranting tones. Sadly, it was not to be. The Union powers-that-be were having no truck with an incognito from the floor of the hall. What had been meticulously planned would be rigorously carried out, and so, although people turned in their seats and stared at the interloper, trying to give a nod to the author of this splendid diversion, and to indicate their agreement with Marcus's intervention, the conference simply ground on, as conferences do. The speaker just smiled condescendingly and began where he had left off.

However, the press had not forgotten. At the end of the morning session there was a rush to surround Marcus and pin him, metaphorically, to the wall. Marcus was the man of the moment. What did he mean about kids being shot? What happened? Did he see himself as a trouble-maker? Did he not believe there was inner-city deprivation? What's all this about rural problems? What problems?

'Look,' said Marcus to the throng, 'the shooting incident got me the publicity and you can root out the story easily – it's well known now all over my county – but what I think you should be investigating is the myth of total rural serenity out there. There is severe rural deprivation as well as the inner-city sort. My kids can't get to see their favourite football teams, or get to pop concerts or any other kind of event – there is almost no rural transport and few shops. There's a great deal more suicide in rural areas than you will be aware of, I reckon, and a lot more domestic violence, because of all the frustration, and anyway, the rustic charm that all of you may subscribe to is getting less and less available to those born in the area – their tied cottages are being sold and turned into twee commuter dwellings or second homes. It's from the newcomers that the myth of rural tranquillity and abundance comes – the real story is somewhat different.'

Marcus had started something. Never again would the rural aspect be used to counter the inner-city problems. Ministers, civil servants, local councillors and local government officers sought his views and support. The case of the shoot and the shootings had done the trick; Elsie's ordeal had led to some good, at least for the national consciousness, and, as it turned out, for Elsie herself. Marcus did not find this out for twenty years, until one day towards the end of his career she turned up at the school with two children in tow.

'I could not leave the old place without seeing you, Headmaster,' she said when she had settled herself and her ten-year-old twins in front of Marcus's desk. 'I never did say a big enough thank you for your concern and for not creating too much of a fuss – just a little fuss.'

'Oh? Thank you, Elsie, but what do you mean "just a little fuss?" I can still see the small scar on your cheek. Surely it merited a much bigger fuss?'

Elsie smiled. 'Your involving the press but not making a big fuss over it put the fear of God into Mr Maltravers, the Head Gamekeeper, and I expect his Lordship was not best pleased either, but the upshot was that the insurance company stopped all their quibbling and doubled the amount of compensation overnight. My mum and dad bought the village shop, me and my three brothers and two sisters all went off to university, as you know, and now we are all nicely placed. I have just come home from Manchester for the weekend. I am a partner in a law firm, with my husband and doing very nicely so I have a lot to thank you and the school for. So, once again thank you.'

Elsie and kids rose to go. 'There is one other thing that incident did for me, Sir.'

'Right. And that is?'

'I stopped smoking immediately afterwards and have never smoked since, so there you are; strange are the ways of the Lord – and I don't mean His Lordship!'

'Well, you know, Elsie, Old Ollie Hutchings hinted to me long ago that you might be trying to give up smoking. He said maybe a good shooting would cure everyone of the habit!'

'Sorry to disappoint him Sir, but actually it was the A and E doctor when Miss McCreadie took me to the hospital. He heard I had been smoking and then insisted on showing me a slide with a picture of a smoker's lung: "Thirty five years old, she was," he said.'

'Do you mean she's dead?' I asked the doctor. "Yes one of many" he told me. So, there you are Sir, That's what did it! Not another cigarette from the day to this. I'm a country lass but I'm no bumkin!'

'That's just what Mr Hutchings said!'

'Well, he was right. I've done very nicely. The only downside is the scar where the doc gouged out the pellet, but I'll settle for that – it's a constant reminder. So thank you again, Sir.'

And with that Elsie took her final bow from Market Upabit.

Marcus sat for a while, musing, then he stretched and in so doing his eye caught sight of one of the many school photos on his wall and a lanky Year 10 fifteen-year-old, with tousled hair, whose perpetual smile shone out at him.

'Jimmy Delafield! Well, I never. I haven't thought about him for many a year. Good job his story never got to the press.' He laughed at the thought. 'Jimmy Delafield, a bus, a drunken fisherman, a screaming little girl, and a copper. That could have been the end of my promising career. I really must write that story down in my notebook.'

The tale of Jimmy Delafield was written down, bringing the 'Rural Deprivation' trilogy to an enigmatic close …

End of the Track

Jimmy Delafield did not resent school. He simply did not like going there. Market Upabit was fifteen miles away and the school bus had to wander through at least ten villages, taking over an hour from the forest area to the school. And even more frustrating, he sighed, was that school and the school journey took out ten hours of each weekday from his beloved time on the family farm.

Jimmy was a born farmer. At age fifteen he was a master of lambing, milking, sowing, hoeing and mowing, not to mention reaping and, above all, tractor driving, manoeuvring his all-time favourite tractor, 'Goldfinger' – so-called because of its potential for evil malpractice.

Father Delafield was perfectly happy with son's predilection (though he wouldn't call it that). 'It's what Jimmy wants to do, Mother, that's all there is to it,' was his response when Mrs Delafield expressed her disappointment at homework missed and time spent away from books.

'He's a farmer and that's the long and short of it.'

Mum was of the mind that reckoned a good education was never wasted, 'not even for a farmer,' she sniffed. 'I prefer to be an educated farmer's wife, than a thick one, and don't you say otherwise, Horace Delafield.' Farmer Delafield was not going to. So Jimmy's head was forced back into his books as often as Mrs Delafield could find him – not an easy task on a four-hundred-acre farm dotted with woods and copses and on the edge of the Middle England forest which straddled Market Upabit's catchment area.

Jimmy was pretty well resigned to enduring school for another year when he reached fifteen, but that did not stop him joining other lads from the village in conspiring to get up at 5.00am one winter's morning after a heavy snowstorm to pack the snow into a two-metre-high barrier across the only lane into the village, to prevent the school bus getting through. It only lasted a day, because ironically Jimmy's dad ordered Jimmy to drive the tractor with the scoop attached to clear the road. Mr Delafield supervised the removal; Jimmy performed the task. It may have been a sort of punishment. But Jimmy revelled in the work and his dad knew he did.

Those days of school respite were few, of course. Jimmy and the twenty or so kids from the Welland valley villages carried on with their daily pilgrimages to Market Upabit. The coach provided for them by the county council contractor, Bills Buses, was old. Not only was it old, it was cold, dirty and driven by a succession of dubious drivers. But it was cheap and managed to pick up and drop off the far-flung fraternity of forest children in reasonable time. And so the council had resisted all attempts by the school and the Parents Association to change the contractor.

The happy band of Foresters were not bothered one way or the other, of course. A bus was a bus and if it took them home it was good enough for them. And it did until one March day.

Duly at 4.00pm a thousand youngsters poured out of Market Upabit School, seven hundred of them making for the convoy of buses lined up in the bus park. Jimmy's Bills Buses coach, one of the two coaches owned by the firm, was not there, and did not arrive until half an hour after the rest had gone. Headteacher, Marcus Brampton, had made fruitless calls to Bill's Buses office, but just as he was about to inform the county council that he was going to ring a rival company, Bill's Buses' omnibus spluttered into the school, appearing out of a blue haze of exhaust fumes.

Nearly all the pupils had said 'Hi' to the driver as they climbed aboard before Jimmy went a step further. 'Where's Freddy, then?'

Freddy was known to them. He was a 'regular' driver and normally scheduled for lucrative old folk's outings, and the fishing parties that were the staple income for the firm. But Freddy had brought them to school that morning so, where was he?

199

'He's not well,' growled their new driver.

'Oh, drunk again, you mean,' replied Jimmy with his no-nonsense jocularity.

'Don't be funny with me. Sit down. We're going.' The unfamiliar driver's speech was odd and his actions clumsy. He pushed Jimmy away and took off – far too fast for Jimmy's liking.

Jimmy sat down with Paula, the only Sixth Former on the bus.

'Not good, Paula. I reckon our driver is either ill or drunk.'

Paula sniffed. 'I expect he and Freddy have been taking another of them fishing groups, left them at the canal and spent the afternoon in a pub.'

'Jimmy contemplated this, then stood up holding the seat in front as the bus swayed along the road out of town. He pulled himself down to the front and leaned over the driver's shoulder.

'Excuse me. Do you know which route to take?'

'Got it on a bit of paper 'ere.' The driver reached for a piece of paper on the dashboard in front of him. It was blank.

'Was 'ere a minute ago.' He looked down on the floor and the bus swerved towards a ditch.

'Look out,' cried Jimmy grasping the back of the driver's seat.

Looking down seemed to make the driver dizzy. He lifted his head and Jimmy could see the man's eyes roll.

'You're drunk, mate,' he whispered into the man's ear. 'You'd better stop.'

'Don't you start accusing me. Get away from 'ere – go on or I'll report you for interfering with the driver – go on, get back there.'

Jimmy stared at him and then re-joined Paula. 'I'll keep an eye on him, Paula. You keep an eye on the kids. They've stopped chattering. I think they are cottoning on.'

The coach moved into the Market Upabit hinterland, dropping students off regularly until there was just a handful left. It was at that moment that the bus started to sway from side to side. Jimmy motioned to Paula to come forward and join him on the front passenger seat, behind the driver.

'This is dangerous, Paula what do you reckon?'

'I'll tell him to stop or I'll report him shall I?'

'Leave it just a minute, Paula. We're coming into Greythorn. Some of the kids get off here – oops, what the heck's going on?'

The bus was picking up speed instead of slowing down.

'Hey, this is a stop,' shouted Paula.

The driver jabbed down on the brake, shooting all the passengers forward fast. One small Year 7 eleven-year-old banged her mouth on the back of the seat in front, let out a yell and started to cry. The driver swung round in his seat. 'Stop that! You're not hurt. Get off those who have to now.' The driver was rocking back and forward. His speech got more slurred and eventually no-one knew what he was saying.

The Greythorn group alighted as fast as they could. Paula stood by the driver's cubby-hole.

'Look, Mister, you're —'

She got no further. The driver banged the separating door to and put his foot on the accelerator. The bus shot down the lane in what was now a rapidly darkening gloom.

Paula turned to Jimmy.

'He's going to kill us at this rate!'

Jimmy helped Paula back into her seat. The rest of the bus had gone quiet. There were now a dozen young eleven- to thirteen-year-olds left besides Paula and Jimmy. The little girl with the bruised mouth was still whimpering.

'I'll go and sit with Priscilla, Jimmy. You keep an eye on Jacky boy up front. Surely he can tell it's dark and these lanes have Z bends?'

The bus was now swaying through the dark forest, miles from the nearest village or farm. Jimmy had been staring at the driver as the light faded and thought he looked even more groggy.

As Paula stumbled her way to the rear, Jimmy decided he had to confront the driver again. He got up but was then thrown onto his back as the coach hit a bollard on a bend. The coach juddered to a stop as though the brake and clutch had not been used. Jimmy picked himself up and found the driver slumped over the wheel. He shouted to Paula.

'Paula, come here quick.' Paula joined him and they stared down at the driver lying unconscious with his head on the steering wheel. They looked at each other. 'What do you reckon, Paula?'

'Drunk as a lord. He isn't going any further!' She looked through the window. 'And neither are we. We're in the middle of the forest. There are no houses for miles, Jimmy – what are we going to do?'

Jimmy thought hard. 'We have two choices, I think. We can sit here and hope a car comes along or our parents get worried and come looking for us – or I drive the bus to the next village, Bullstone.'

'You can't do that Jimmy. You don't have a licence and you are only fifteen.'

'Nearly sixteen,' protested Jimmy, 'but driving the bus is easy. When you've driven as many tractors as me, a bus is a piece of cake.'

Just then the situation started to dawn on the young pupils at the back. They moved forward. The bus was now almost dark, just the barest of interior lighting. Outside was pitch black. Dolly Close began to cry. Duane Goddard was not sympathetic: 'Oh shut up Dolly, stop crying.' This made Dolly cry more, and louder. She could contain herself no longer and let out a terrifying scream.

'Aaaaarh! I want my Mummy and Daddy, Paula. I'm scared.'

Paula put her arm around her and sat with her. She made her mind up.

'Right. This is what we're going to do. The driver has fallen ill. We can't just stay here. I have authorised Jimmy to drive the bus to Bullstone. We can get help there.'

'Jimmy can't drive, Paula! He'll kill us all.' This from Year 9 Fenella. 'I'm getting off and walking home.'

'Don't be daft, Fennie, it's more dangerous walking then Jimmy driving. He'll drive very slowly and I promise that if we meet another vehicle, we'll stop and get help okay?' Fenella accepted the compromise. The remainder sat down, but in a bunch at the front.

'Let's get this bloke out of the seat and onto the front seat, shall we?' Jimmy was warming to the task.

Jimmy settled himself in the driver's seat and set off. He felt entirely comfortable. Just like his beloved tractor.

'Jimmy I live up Field Lane over there,' said Fenella after a mile or two. 'Can you drop me off here?'

'How far up there?'

'It's less than a mile, Jimmy.'

'Then I'm definitely not dropping you off. I'm going to take you up to the crossroads. You'll only have a few yards to walk then and you can get your mum and dad to ring my mum and dad and tell 'em what's happened – the number's in the phone book.'

Paula looked aghast. 'But shouldn't we just stop Jimmy and ring for help?'

'Paula, by the time we've walked up there with Fennie and her dad has rung for help I can drop most of you at your houses and stop mass parental panic.'

And that is precisely what Jimmy Delafield did. It took him less than half an hour to deposit all of them safely in their villages or farms. The last was Paula, and Jimmy agreed to park there, let Paula and parents arrange for help and to inform Bill's Buses, maybe even the police.'

'You were great, Jimmy,' said Paula and her parents when all that had been done and Mr Delafield had arrived to pick him up. 'Troubles over then?' said Mr. Delafield in his usual cheerful and optimistic way.

Well, they were in a way, but not for Marcus Brampton and Market Upabit School.

Marcus got the story first from Jimmy as soon as he got to the school. Father Delafield and son were already there. The saga was spelled out.

'You probably know the police warned Jimmy that they would be back when they picked the coach up yesterday evening.'

Marcus hadn't, but he nodded and Mr. Delafield continued.

'Jimmy may have done wrong technically, Headmaster, but he did right by a lot of children, remember that – probably done the school's reputation a lot of good, too.'

'Look, I can tell you I am very proud of Jimmy and will support him to the hilt if too many questions are asked. We have to accept that Jimmy acted illegally but everything went well and all the children are safe. That is the long and short of it. Leave it with me, Mr Delafield and Jimmy, off you go to registration and well done.'

When Jimmy and Mr Delafield had left, Marcus sat for a moment ruminating, and then picked up the phone to the main Fenborough Police Station.

'Brampton, Headmaster, Market Upabit School here. Can I speak to someone involved in the Bill's Buses incident yesterday.'

'Ah, Headmaster I was just going to telephone you to tell you Superintendent Yallop is on his way to see you.'

'What, the Superintendent? Eustace Yallop? Goodness, okay. Thanks, I'll speak to him shortly.'

As soon as Marcus put the phone down, the door to his office opened and there stood the school receptionist. She was about to announce the visitor when an immaculately uniformed Eustace Yallop stepped out from behind her, just like Doctor Who appearing out of the Tardis.

Superintendent Yallop was not one to dilly-dally. 'I haven't much time, Mr Brampton. I just need the briefest of chats with you.'

'Right, take a seat,' said Marcus, but the Super already had.

'Now, we both know enough of the detail of young Jimmy's activities to get straight down to it. The prosecution of the coach company and driver is all in hand and has nothing to do with you. It will take its course. What we need to discuss is the matter of young Jimmy.'

'Yes,' said Marcus anxious to get in with a quick bit of support. 'What a splendid job he did, didn't he?' That should deflect any immediate criticism, thought Marcus.

'Don't try the soft-soaping, Headmaster I haven't got time.' Marcus felt chastised. The Superintendent pushed on. 'Don't say anything more, just listen to what I have to say. I have a decision to make and you have a problem to overcome.' At that last point Superintendent Yallop jabbed a finger towards Marcus.

Marcus sat up. 'I've got a problem? Why is that? I know enough about the law to know that what goes on during coach rides home is not my problem: the people responsible are the

205

county council, the bus company and the parents, I understand.'

'That's not the problem. You're not under any legal pressure, but nevertheless your job is on the line – don't you realise that?'

Marcus stared hard at the Super. Was he being serious? 'What on earth do you mean?'

The Superintendent finally took his cap off and put it on the desk in front of Marcus. He leaned back and tapped his fingers together. A bit of a showman, thought Marcus. Yallop continued. He suddenly leaned forward. 'I take it you are intent on backing young Jimmy to the hilt: a bit of a hero, Custer riding in with the Seventh Cavalry and all that, did nothing seriously wrong, kids all delivered home safely, eh?'

He was right. Marcus felt a little bit of discomfort creeping up him, but he stayed silent.

'You're a big supporter of the upholding of the law, aren't you, Mr Brampton? Very voluble on the subject if my memory serves me right. Isn't that so?'

'What are you getting at, Superintendent?'

'Last year you were all for throwing the legal book at gamekeeper Maltravers and His Lordship, weren't you? Criticised the police and me for taking a soft approach?'

'Well, it did seem to me to be a clear case of gross negligence, shooting nine kids, don't you think?'

'It's a point of view, Mr Brampton, and so I take it that in the interests of consistency you will now be calling for young Jimmy to be prosecuted for his blatant breaking of the law and reckless behaviour in risking injury, even death, to nine young children. Isn't that so?'

Marcus could see which way the wind was blowing but not what to do about it. 'There are some clear differences, Superintendent.'

'Oh, there always are differences Headmaster, but the simple fact is that you were scathing about our softly-softly approach towards blatant law-breaking, which happened to be MY decision and which I took all the flack for. As I say, you were scathing about it even though Maltravers and His Lordship were wetting their pants over it and even though my approach produced a larger amount of compensation for young Elsie than she could ever have imagined.'

He paused and scrutinised Marcus's discomfort. 'So, I assume you will support to the hilt our prosecution of this new malefactor, new breaker of our precious laws, eh?'

'I'm afraid I have given my word to Mr Delafield that I would support Jimmy to the full.'

'Ah, so double standards are okay, are they Headmaster? Your governors and the general public will be delighted about that won't they? I see trouble ahead. A lot of bad publicity for the school. Oh dear.'

'There'll be trouble if I criticise young Jimmy as well.'

Yallop leaned even closer to Marcus.

'Then, as I say, Headmaster, you've got a problem – a big problem. This is what being top man leads to, eh?'

Marcus felt uncomfortably sweaty. He wriggled in his chair but said nothing. Then to his astonishment he saw a huge smile break over the Superintendent's face.

'I can't keep it up any longer, Marcus – can I call you Marcus? Well, never mind, I'll call you Marcus because you and I are going to join in a little legitimate conspiracy.'

'We are?'

'Yes, it's quite simple. You'll simply keep quiet, very quiet – no pompous, self-righteous comments about my way of working. You'll make no comments at all. You'll hide behind the accused's prime line of defence: "No comment. It is in the hands of the police, so I cannot possibly comment." That's all you have to do. And as for me, Jimmy will be given a 'right talking to' as befits a wayward fifteen-year-old (and a secret pat on the back), the press will be told that they cannot publish a fifteen-year-old's name, and the locals can laud and praise him as much and as long as they like. You look good, school looks good. Do I make myself clear?'

'As clear as your Sergeant was when he saw me after the shooting incident.'

'Yes, indeed, but you didn't take any notice, did you? However, if you don't this time then all sorts of "information" might find its way to the local rags – not something either of us would like, eh, Headmaster?'

The Superintendent thrust out a hand. 'Let's shake and I'll be off.' Marcus knew he had no alternative.

It must have been a week later that Jimmy brought him a note from father Delafield.

It simply said:

'Brilliant Mr Brampton. The police called on us and had a word with Jimmy and me and his mum. They explained the law and warned him not to do it again. No further action they said, so I said a big thank you to the police, but the Sergeant said don't thank us, thank the Headmaster. So, Jimmy will pass on our thanks, and Mrs Delafield says I must tell you what a good Headmaster you are, very clever.'

PERIOD FOUR:
TEST 'EM ALL

Dental Records

Marcus Brampton was sitting in his office preparing his morning assembly. He remembers it well. It's a funny thing; he always remembered with great clarity his confrontations with 'the law'. He was just penning a suitable blessing for the final flourish at the assembly when his secretary, Brenda, popped her head round the door. 'Two uniformed gentlemen are in Reception wanting to see you, Headmaster. They say it's a bit urgent.'

'O Lor', and assembly is in five minutes. Can you ask them if they can wait till after morning assembly is over? Thanks.'

'Sorry, Headmaster,' came a voice from behind her, 'we really do need to see you. Now.'

Two of the force's burliest PCs kitted out with all the modern paraphernalia brushed past Brenda and filled the space available. Brenda did not wait. She was off to alert the Deputy. She could sense that the law beats assembly and assembly waits for no man pinned in his room by two bobbies.

Marcus was not one to delay constables in their duty. He dropped his assembly prep and put on another head-magisterial hat: participating in crime solving. He was sure that was what it would be. He could not imagine any other reason for the visit. The sergeant took his cap off and handed Marcus, without explanation and with a dramatic thrust, a somewhat ragged card, originally white but now a kind of dirty grey. Marcus twisted it around in his fingers and then looked enquiringly at the sergeant.

'Looks like some kind of visiting card, no?'

'It's an appointment card for the dentist, Sir.'

'Yes … and?'

'Not important in itself, perhaps, sir,' sniffed the other copper, 'but we've just found it on the back seat of a stolen car – just outside your school.'

'Yes … and?'

The sergeant came to life now. 'It's an appointment card in the name of one Silas Burton. He's one of your pupils, Headmaster.'

'Yes, he is, Sergeant. How did you know that?'

The policeman sniffed again and began to count off on his fingers. 'We know him, we know his brother Tyrone, his sister Vivien, his dad Ivan, his uncle Doug and two cousins. Regulars they are.'

'Ah, yes,' said Marcus with a sigh, 'I thought it wouldn't be long before Silas graduated.' Not a very witty riposte but Marcus was now wishing he hadn't so readily agreed to this chance meeting with no time to consider its import and, more importantly, prepare how he was going to control it. He did not like shopping his pupils to the police without some careful thought – and on his own terms.

'Well, Sir, we're going to have a little word with Silas up the road before he gets to the school. So we wanted you to know why he'll be late this morning – or absent.' He added the last throwaway remark with just a touch of menace.

'You're sure all this is legit procedure, sergeant? I think I ought to check it with the inspector, shouldn't I?'

'No need for that, Sir. Just wasting your time. We're just going to have this little word with him, just seeing what he has got to say about this card, you know. Just that.'

'Well,' Marcus said, mulling this over, 'I really ought to inform Mrs Burton, his mother. That's for sure. She has struggled to keep her husband and boys on the right track, you know. A losing battle but she never stops trying.'

'Yes, we know that. By all means ring her. By the time she gets here I expect our little chat with Silas will be over.'

They both rose. 'We'll be off now. Silas will be nearby by now.'

And so off they went. They had barely gone a minute or two before Angie put through a phone call from Mrs Burton.

'She sounds very anxious, Headmaster. Do you want to speak to her?'

'Yes, put her on. I was going to ring her anyway.'

A loud and excitable Mrs Burton came on the line. 'Headmaster, tell me what's going on. I've just had a call from Silas on his mobile. He says two coppers have stopped him. What for?'

Marcus hesitated for a moment, did not think he was letting out any secrets, so told her. 'Well, Mrs Burton, it seems to be something about a stolen car.'

There was a verbal explosion at the other end.

'That's plain daft!' she cried down the phone. 'It can't be Silas. It's not possible. That's not his line. That's his brother, our Tyrone, he does stealin' cars!'

'Well, that's odd,' said Marcus. 'The police have found a dental appointment card in the car with Silas's name on it.'

'Well, I'll be blowed!' she cried after a short pause. 'We've been looking for that everywhere!'

O dear, O dear

One day, was quietly minding my own business, said Marcus, a call was put through to me from a very irate member of the public in far-off Wiltshire who loosed off a tirade about comprehensive school yobs, 'from your school!' he yelled. 'They intimidated me and my wife and ruined my enjoyment of a play at Stratford yesterday evening. They made us feel quite ill. So, I'm alerting you, on behalf of my wife and myself, of my intention to inform the authorities. Officially. And get the Royal Shakespeare Theatre to ban future parties from your school'.

He ended by yelling, 'You'll be hearing from me,' after which he banged the phone down before I could say a word. I then made a few discrete enquiries and was ready to answer his follow-up letter.

The letter listed in full his complaints: boys talking all the way through; cans of lager being consumed and being passed 'back and forth'; groups of boys leaving the auditorium for the toilet during the performance; one boy sitting next to him in Row E shouting 'What a prat!' after one of Launcelot Gobbo's exits; one boy accompanied Portia in an impromptu duet of her 'quality of mercy' speech; and, to cap it all, no member of staff seemed able to keep a check. 'It made us feel quite poorly,' he ended.

Serious stuff indeed – except that he had got the wrong school!

The theatre had given him the name of one of our town's six schools, but the wrong one! We did not have a party at Stratford that day, but one of the three local independent schools did! And, as I ascertained from the theatre manager, it was a party from one of them which had occupied the said seats – but not before he had started berating me for the aberrant behaviour of obvious hooligans from my school who

214

had no idea how to behave in a public place of entertainment and who had made members of the general public ill from worry about their physical well-being. He thought he would have to ban future parties 'from your establishment.' He could scarcely cope with the mere mention of a complaint from a member of the public about a school party. That was clear.

'I am so sorry you feel that a ban is in order,' I said rather mischievously.

'I do not think we have any alternative,' he replied haughtily. 'We have our loyal clientele to consider.'

I let him go on for a while before asking him politely if he had checked which school was actually occupying that block of seats. There was a long silence and then a despairing 'Ooooooh d-e-a-r – it seems it wasn't your party but it was from your town!' I am not sure whether he thought that I was guilty by association, but I did not wait to find out. I was pretty fed up myself at that point.

'I suppose you have now noted that the party is likely to come from the large, and very prestigious independent school in the town? It is such a pity that you are going to ban their future parties. It will come as a shock to the local MP who was a boy there – oh, and a former Deputy Governor of the Bank of England as well, but there we are, you must take drastic action, I do appreciate that.' I was feeling more mischievous now!

There was another long pause.

'I only said I *thought* we would have to.' I could almost smell the sweat from his brow.

'No, Sir, you said you thought you had no alternative, but I think you are right to think again – very wise. I am sure the school will take appropriate action when you've informed the Head. No one would like to see a ban on future parties for the misdeeds of this bad set of high-spirited young gentlemen, and I'm sure you and your colleagues would have come to the same conclusion with respect to a local comprehensive school's 'hooligans' like mine now, wouldn't you?'

'O yes, yes. Certainly. I was just feeling a bit … upset, you know.'

'Well, so am I, but let's leave the matter.'

You can imagine how I enjoyed writing a 'polite' letter back to the complainant (although, to be fair, the mis-identity was not his fault), requesting that he should enquire from the theatre which school it actually was. I received no reply, but later I was invited by the Head of the independent school to meet and to receive his apologies, which I did.

Over a glass of his sherry, we were able to agree that all schools coped with a range of activities/responsibilities/problems and we commiserated with each other about trying to be teachers/managers/psychologists/policemen/detectives/judges/financiers/estate agents and so on. It was a good evening for both of us.

We ended up in complete agreement that it was the most exciting of jobs, and a privilege to roll along with it in life's 'diurnal course' but it did occasionally have its downsides!

A Testing Time

Most Year 3 classes are memorable. They are no longer 'the little ones'
feeling their way nor yet fully-fledged juniors. They can look down on
the Reception class, and take no notice of the juniors above them.
They are generally knowing, critical and talkative. Some would
indeed talk the hind legs off a donkey – but not before they had found
out the donkey's name, who was pulling it apart, and why. Grace
Archdale told Marcus a delightful story of her most memorable class
of six- and seven-year-olds – led by Maisie, who, she confidently
predicted, could have a successful career as a sergeant major or leader
of HM's Opposition or any other position that requires her to turn
opponents into quivering heaps. Over a pot of tea, she told me what
had happened 'when an inspector called'.

My first ever experience of an Ofsted inspection was just before
the end of my first term as a Newly Qualified Teacher and as a
Year 2 class teacher. When the Head announced at a staff
meeting that just before Christmas there was going to be this
awe-inspiring event, I remember a collective groan, and a sense
of impending doom settle over my dozen or so colleagues. Tea-
cups rattled nervously, and magazines slipped off knees
unobserved. It was a novel experience for me as I had been
used to a lively, carefree and humorous lot of colleagues before
this day. But no-one seemed to find anything witty to say.
Personally, I felt no concern at all. I was learning the ropes day
by day, period by period. Another person peering at my class
and making notes to help me along was no big deal, or so I
thought until the first day of the week-long inspection, which
was the normal period for those days.

The staff were gathered in the staffroom just before
registration and the daily assembly, while support staff looked
after the kids. The lead inspector, appropriately but

unexpectedly named Cyrus Judge, wanted us to meet him and his team and, according to the Head, reassure us.

Well, he met us all right but as to reassuring us, that was another matter. He began by simply announcing, 'I'm Judge by name, judge by occupation and judge by inclination.' He paused for the expected laugh, but I heard only a single short titter and that came from one of his team. So he continued, I kid you not, by staring at the front row and declaring, 'If you're wondering what the point of this inspection is, let me explain it to you in the words of the great Duke of Wellington at Waterloo: 'Your duty is not to reason why, yours is to do and die.'

'It wasn't Wellington, and it wasn't Waterloo,' said a small voice from the back. It was our Deputy Head and learned historian, Anna Dyne.

'Well, some other General then, at some other time,' replied Judge, laughing it off without batting an eyelid. 'The point I'm making is that you must not spend the week trying to work out what we are inspecting and then adjusting your teaching accordingly. Just get on with teaching classes as you do all the time. Just pretend we are not there. We are well trained to blend into the background. Any questions you might have please address them to the Head. We will be liaising with him constantly during the week.'

The Head stopped me on the way out of the staff room. 'Grace. Just a moment. Mr Judge is with me for the first part of the morning, but then wants to see your lesson after mid-morning break. Can you pick him up at my office? Thanks.'

I can't remember what my reaction to this surprising news was. But I do remember collecting Mr Judge and escorting him down the corridor – trying on the way to demonstrate my confidence and lack of concern that the top man himself was starting off the inspection week with me.

'I suppose you're an Infant specialist,' I queried, thinking that this would be an easy opener.

'Oh no,' he replied. 'I haven't been in an Infant class before – not since I was a child myself. I have been a secondary school art and craft teacher for thirty years, a Head of what they call Design and Technology these days. My inspection team of six is a mixture of secondary and primary, but my expert in Infants is looking at another of your colleagues this period – science, I think. But I thought it was appropriate for me to attend your class since I noted on the lesson plan that you were doing some elementary craft work today. Isn't that so?'

'Yes, I am,' I said.

I should have shut up there and then, but I suddenly felt rather indignant. I got the impression that Mr Judge was looking down on Infant teachers as art and craft interlopers, lacking in specific expertise, and so I bridled.

'But won't you find it rather difficult inspecting an infant department if your whole experience has been in secondary education?' I enquired. I did not even try to suppress my indignation. Not a vestige of a sweet smile.

'I don't think so,' he said, without a pause. 'A teacher is a teacher, is a teacher I always say. We inspectors are trained to be versatile, you know. You can rely on me to size things up and come pretty quickly to a well-honed *judgement*.' And he had the effrontery to laugh at his own witty play on his name!

So at that point I did shut up. I could not trust myself!

Just before we got to my classroom, he piped up again. 'I see you're using scissors for cutting coloured paper this period. I hope you have done a risk assessment and a risk management plan. Perhaps I could have a copy.'

Inwardly my heart stopped beating and my brain froze. A risk management plan! They were only five- and six-year-olds! And using blunt scissors with rounded points. He didn't really want a ten-page written assessment, did he?!

But then I realised that he was right. There were risks. Every period of every day there are particular and peculiar risks with little ones. That was reality. That was life. Rapid thoughts went through my mind. Will I be telling Maisie not to snip off the ends of Peggy's pigtails? Of course I will! I do it every craft period! And does she take any notice? Just for a moment, no longer. She will almost certainly have to grace the naughty step, unless she is overawed by the presence of an inspector, and she will once again miss out on the Smarties for good work. And will I then have to prevent her pinching Penny's Smarties? Of course I will!

And will I have to tell Danny to stop flicking Rohan's ear with his pencil? Of course I will. I did yesterday as I did the day before. I can hear myself saying, 'No, Danny, Rohan does *not* have a flea in his ear and no, Danny, neither do you. No, it's not what your mother meant. It's just an itch and you can rub it gently with your finger. It does not require a ruler in one ear and a pencil in another. No, it did not work yesterday, Danny.' I sighed and smiled to myself. This is Infant school teaching.

'And no, Milton, Joey does not want to be an Apache. No, not even Geronimo. nor Crazy Horse either. Just put the blue wax crayon down, Milton, and, Joey, you go and clean your face and arms with a Kleenex tissue. No, it does not look good at all. It's not good for your skin. Because I say so, Joey, and your mother will too, if she sees it. Don't argue – I know she'll be furious. Again. No, it won't make any difference if you are Sitting Bull. Whether he was a hero or not is neither here nor there, Joey. Yes I know we read about them in *Heroes and Heroines*. You can play them in our drama lesson later.' I could not help wondering what would happen when we got to *Wizards and Witches* after Christmas! And almost certainly we would!

I snapped out of my reverie when Mr Judge addressed me again, as we entered the classroom. 'Well?' he asked.

I was about to enquire 'Well, what?' when I remembered he had asked me for a copy of my risk management plan.

'Of course, Sir. It will be with you before you leave school today.'

'Highly satisfactory. Now just leave me to wander round and take notes. I shall be able to draw my own conclusions while observing.'

With that he set off for the tables at the far end of the room, greeting my classroom assistant, Maggie, as he passed. So far none of the children had paid him the slightest attention, so absorbed were they in their cutting and pasting. Then he made the fatal mistake of saying loudly, 'Good morning, boys and girls.'

The silence was broken.

'Mornin', Sir.'

''Ow do.'

'Wotcha.'

''Ow are you?'

'Good bye.'

'Ta-ra.'

And, of course, having got going the greetings went round again.

''Ow do.'

'Good mornin'.'

'Wotcha.'

'Nice day, Sir.'

'Ta-ra.'

It was like church bells ringing from all parts of the city, but not so mellifluous! My inspector colleague was caught unawares. But just before the third round began, I decided to intervene.

'All right. That'll do. It was very nice of you to welcome our inspector visitor. Now get on with your work. You have a lot to do.'

Mr Judge nodded his thanks to me.

But the damage had been done. The inner world they had inhabited before we entered had been invaded. There was now a subdued but excited buzz. I bent over the table of four I was at, and tried to absorb myself in their activity, but my ears would not stop wagging. Someone was going to make the first move, and sure enough it was Maisie. Little Maisie with the smiley round face and even rounder wire spectacles, through which she blinked with disarming innocence. She leaned back on her chair, stared at Mr Judge and pointed her crayon straight at him.

'So, are you a spectre then?'

'No, you mean inspect —' He got no further.

'He's not a spectre, our Maisie,' said her table companion, Peggy. 'Spectres are ghosts. Miss Archdale read a story about them last week from our reader, *Ghosts and ghouls*. Remember?'

'No, you don't understand,' cried Mr Judge, a certain amount of desperation entering his voice, 'I am an IN-spector.'

This temporarily stopped the table in its tracks. Danny asked the question they were all dying to ask.

'Well, if you are an IN-spector, what's an OUT-spector do?'

'No, no, there are no OUT-spectors, just IN-spectors, like me.'

'What do IN-spectors do, then?' asked Peggy.

'Well, they come into school and observe what you do.' It was a bit of a lame explanation and Maisie was not going to let him get away with it.

'That's not much of a job, is it?' She looked around and got the nods from her table companions. 'My dad has a real job. He works in the quarry.'

'So does mine,' said Danny.

'And mine,' echoed Reggie next to him. Others joined in. Most dads worked in or for the quarry.

'My dad hasn't got a job,' growled Peggy. 'Not since Danny's dad blew him up!'

'No, he didn't! Your dad should have moved away when the hooter blew. Everybody knows that.'

Disputes about life in the quarry were not rare! I decided not to intervene. Mr Judge could devise his own escape plan.

'That will do now, children. I am very sorry to hear about your father and I hope he will soon be back at work. Now shall we get on. You have a lot of work to do.' Mr Judge was learning fast.

There was a general subsiding of voices, but I heard Peggy mutter, 'My dad won't go back to work. He gets his cards every day.' Mr Judge cut in. 'I think you mean "He *got* his cards" – made redundant – don't you?'

'Redcurrant!' cried Peggy in high dudgeon, 'My dad won't like that! He's black. You can see that if you look at me! You shouldn't say things like that!'

'No, you've got it wrong. I didn't say "redcurrant". I said he was "redundant".' Mr Judge now realised he had used a word beyond the comprehension of Year 2. 'It means "lost his job". That's what "got his cards" means, you see.' Mr Judge on the backfoot again.

'No it doesn't,' said Peggy, obviously totally puzzled. 'I said he *gets* his cards every day, and that's what I meant. He gets his pack of cards, and his box, and his matches, and takes them with him down to the Quarryman's Arms and plays canasta with his pals every morning till it's dinner-time.' She turned to her table companions, 'Do you know what this 'spector bloke is on about? He's lost me.'

'Naaaw,' said Maisie, drawing it out in disdain and shaking her head. 'No wonder my mum says we shouldn't speak to strange men.'

Mr Judge was just standing there swapping his big black book from hand to hand. 'Welcome to the Infants,' I thought.

I did not catch the next exchange. Maggie, my assistant, had sidled across to me. 'Sorry, Grace. I had to let Pansy go to the toilet. She was desperate.'

'Oh dear! Not to worry, Maggie. She often forgets to go before school. Always too busy.'

I appeared calm but my inner thoughts were building up again. Vision of Pansy bouncing through the door. 'What is the first thing we do when we have been to the toilet, Pansy? Yes, that's right, we pull our knickers up. *Before* we get back to the classroom! No, you are not missing anything if you take the time to smooth down your skirt.'

Just then the door opened, and in walked Pansy, utterly prim and completely dressed. Not a trace of blue knickers. Triumph!

'Well done, Pansy,' I whispered as she skipped past me. 'You see, you can remember to make yourself tidy sometimes.'

'Yes, Miss, I can. A lady with a big book walking in the corridor with the 'eadmaster just told me what I was showing just as I got to the door. That was lucky, wasn't it?'

'I hope so,' I thought.

I took the opportunity at this point to whisper to Maggie to nip along to the Head and implore him to find, write or otherwise provide a risk assessment for the use of scissors in an infant art class and to slip it into the bundle of inspectors' information. All corners covered now.

Meanwhile Mr Judge seemed intent on regaining the initiative. He was speaking to Maisie. That was a mistake, too.

Maisie had stuck a big red circle onto her white card, with one yellow triangle sticking up straight out of the top, two long orange rectangles protruding left and right and two more big green rectangles hanging from the bottom capped by a yellow square at each end.

'That's a nice hot sun with colourful rays,' said Mr Judge in his encouraging voice.

Maisie, with an instinctive sense of drama, laid down her scissors, put her hands firmly on either side of her card and turned her head slowly upwards to fix the hapless inspector in her gaze. Her eyes were blinking through the large round circles of her spectacles. Indignation was writ large.

'That is *not* a sun and these are not rays,' she said with a hint of contempt. 'That's our teacher, Miss Archdale.'

'Ah, yes, now you tell me, I can see it is the teacher. Very good, but why has she only got one ear sticking out of the top?'

'It's not an ear! That's her hair done up in a bun.'

She pointed her finger at the inspector. 'You don't have one ear on the top of your head, do you? You must know some funny people, you must. Ears are at the side of everyone's head in this class.' She looked round the table at the nodding heads.

'And I haven't stuck the ears on yet 'cos I am just cutting out two more triangles,' she added.

'Oh, jolly good. I suppose you will be adding eyes, nose and mouth later.' Mr Judge was trying hard to retrieve the situation, and I smiled as I shuffled round the adjacent table relishing the encounter behind me.

'No. I won't be adding any mouth or nose or anything else because we haven't got those temp things – what are they, Danny?'

'Templates.'

'Yes, that's it. We don't have any of those cardboard template things for a mouth or nose, so you have to imagine them.'

'Well,' said Mr Judge, still in the middle of extricating himself from an artistic mire. 'You could draw them on with your felt-tip pen.'

This was just too much for Maisie and the other children, too. There was a general muttering of youthful revolution.

'You can't do that. This is a cut and paste lesson!'

'That's not allowed! That's crayoning!'

'That would be cheating!'

Mr Judge gave in. He might have been a bit pompous, but he was at heart a kind and caring man. Before he moved on, he attempted one more move for rapport.

'Thank you for your conversation … err … what's your name?' He was addressing Maisie.

'We're Table Four,' replied Maisie slowly and suspiciously. 'We don't give our own names to strangers'.

Mr Judge smiled. 'I don't think I count as a stranger, do I?'

I think he realised as soon as he said it that Table Four would not miss the chance.

Maisie looked round her pals and wagged her crayon at each of them in turn. 'He's been a bit strange, hasn't he? Just popping in here, interrupting our work?' Naturally the others agreed unanimously nodding heads vigorously. So Maisie reported back to Mr Judge. 'We all think it's a bit strange you coming in here for a few minutes and then going away. I expect you'll say we're all daft, won't you?'

'No, certainly not … err … Table Four you have been most interesting. In fact, I think you are a credit to your teacher.'

I could have hugged him and them for that. I gave him full marks for his perspicacity, although I suspected that nobody would be terribly interested in my estimation of inspectors.

'I am sure Miss Archdale is proud of you and I can see you like her.'

I appreciated that gesture, too.

'Yes, we do,' they chorused.

At the end of the morning, when inspectors and kids had left, I wandered round the tables looking at the range of picture cut-outs. I left Table Number Four to the end. I do not know why, but probably because in my bones I knew that Maisie would have the last word. And so she did.

Neatly laid out in her place were two pictures: one of a red face, orange arms and green-stockinged legs, entitled 'Teacher', and next to it a grey paper with a royal blue circle, three black triangles on top, two yellow squares at the side, two red rectangular arms, and two columns of green squares dangling down from the circle to the bottom edge of the paper. On the blue circle were drawn – in black felt-tip – two dots for eyes, two oversize black ovals staring out like a Tamworth pig, and a thin sliver of white sticky paper for a mouth. It was entitled boldly at the top in black felt-tip, 'A SPECTER'.

Inspectors are not immune from inspection. Judge not that ye be not judged, Mr Judge.

Her Majesty Inspects

One of the least looked-forward to activities that are the lot of Headteachers are visits by inspectors. Both Much Knowing Primary and Market Upabit Academy have had their share of visits. They are not generally remembered as times of frivolity or even just good humour, but they have made many a contribution to 'la comédie pédagogique'.

Marcus Brampton, Head of Market Upabit School, now an academy, remembered the visit to his school of a group of Her Majesty's Inspectors, prior to the institution of OFSTED, the Office for Standards in Education. It was to carry out a full school inspection. HMI were very experienced, professional officials, working for the government but independent of it. They had the task of inspecting schools on behalf of the government, but also carried messages and examples of good practice from other schools they had inspected – something that OFSTED inspectors are not briefed to do.

Teachers, like anyone else whose activities are being closely scrutinised, were apprehensive about their arrival on the scene but knew that they would be engaging in a professional conversation about their teaching and how, if at all, it could be improved. And, anyway, there were not that many of them, so the likelihood of a full-scale inspection was remote.

Her Majesty's Inspectors were also a rather social lot, who having had to work solo for much of their year, looked forward to a group school inspection so that they could spend a week in agreeable professional, like-minded company.

Marcus knew all that, and so, when the lead HMI asked for the name of a good hotel in the town, he was ready to oblige. Luckily there was only one, and a very good, comfortable one, the 'Lord Roger', in Market Upabit town square. Even more fortunately it was managed by one of the parents of a sixth former at the school and was almost wholly staffed by ex- and present students of Market Upabit School.

Now, you may be under the impression that waiters are always on the move. and not waiting, was it were. They always appear to be doing their serving, clearing away, and tidying up and presenting bills, with unseeing eyes and unhearing ears, but do not be deceived. Waiters see and hear *everything*. Inscrutably, intensively and inevitably. When looking over shoulders to serve vegetables, their ears will pick up any murmured remark or aside. When brushing crumbs off the table-cloth at the end of a meal, their eyes will take in any notes lying on the table.

And the maître d' standing by the main door in attendance is not, as might appear, peering at the flaking plaster on the ceiling. He, or indeed she, is taking in the nuances of the scene, noting who sits where, who has the ear of the chief diner, who is the know-all ignored by the rest, who is down in starvation corner (usually the silent and thoughtful newcomer to the team), and most importantly which ones have the ear of the lead person. All these details can be passed on for processing by whoever needs to process them. John Milton, in a 1678 sonnet, wrote: 'They also serve who only stand and wait.' One can only conclude that he had frequented a fair number of good Restoration restaurants.

At the time of the Market Upabit inspection it was the manager who was chief nark, Mr Big, the loyal parent, whose phone call to the Head was scheduled for early the following morning.

Thus it was that when the group of nine of Her Majesty's Inspectors took their three-course dinners and wines around the oak table in the seventeenth-century private dining room their every word about that day's inspection and the following day's targets had been noted, passed to the manager, sifted and written down. And so, by the appointed time, edited details were relayed by surreptitious telephone by 'person unknown' to the Head at his breakfast table.

Thus it was that at the 8.45am pre-school meeting with the lead inspector Marcus Brampton was able to remark with a casual air, 'Well, after yesterday's inspections, Mr Watchet, I expect you will be doing as I would do, observing carefully how well we are doing at such and such and so on, and would want to look at this and that.' Marcus accurately and skilfully mentioned the very stuff of the HMI discussion the night before.

The lead inspector's eyes widened and mouth gaped. He was impressed, as indeed he was meant to be, by the professional perspicacity of the Head. And to the joy of all – both the inspectors and the inspected – everyone was able to relish the next day's classroom observations. What the inspectors were looking for was no surprise to the teachers; what the teachers knew and did was a great surprise to HMI.

The Head had even been told the joke that the lead inspector had made as the post-prandial port and brandies were doing their rounds. 'Do you know,' the lead inspector had asked of his colleagues, having put up his hand to silence the post-prandial chatter. 'Do you know – if all the sociologists coming out of universities were laid head to toe across the Sahara desert …' He spread his arms out to indicate the length of each body and then paused as if waiting for an answer of which none was forthcoming, '… it would be a jolly good thing!'

He burst out laughing at his own joke followed by congratulatory guffaws from his companions. Even the young waiter was infected by the convivial laughter and repeated the joke to all the other sixth form waiters. Hence it arrived at the Head's office along with all the other intelligence reports from the school spies.

Marcus was able to slip into the morning conversation with the lead man a small detail about the school having looked into the advisability of introducing Sociology into the sixth form curriculum but had decided not to go ahead for the time being. He hoped that decision met with HMI approval.

'Absolutely, Headmaster. Absolutely. Not quite the right time, we feel.'

Marcus felt it circumspect not to point out that they were actually in favour of Sociology as a sixth-form subject, but could not find a sociology graduate to teach it despite HMI's view that the country was swimming in them.

'How wise,' said the lead HMI. 'Very good decision.' And he made a note in his folder.

Marcus felt another plus mark coming on. He was not disappointed. An outstanding report followed noting, inter alia, 'the astute managerial qualities' of the Head. Marcus pondered this unusual remark. He had a shrewd suspicion that the 'astute managerial qualities' embellishment was a subtle hint that the inspectors had worked out the school's espionage ploy! He never did find out the truth.

The Inspector Inspected

'Every school has its characters, don't they?' Ruth asked her friends gathered in The Babbling Brook.

'That was certainly my experience, Ruth,' said Clive 'Dan' Dare next to her. 'I met dozens in my career, but the most memorable was one I encountered in an inner-city school where I was Head of English. This chap had entertained generations of students with his antics, but it wasn't his bizarre teaching methods that I remember; it was their sudden collapse when he came up against his nemesis – Year 8.

'He had never met a group that was solidly and stolidly impervious to his zaniness, and he couldn't cope! He was so exasperated by the universal passivity of his Year 8 class, its uniform dullness, its collective will not to annoy Sir or Miss, and its simple obsession with just being nice, that on the spur of the moment, after his fifth question about the rhythm of a Beatles lyric had been met with total silence, he threw his book on the floor, leapt onto the nearest table, crouched down, started to flap his bent arms like a demented farmyard bird and clucked, "Look at me! I'm a chicken!"

'It was the last straw for my colleague: he resigned the next day and moved to Alaska, remarking at his leaving do that he looked forward to the opportunity to talk to himself without thirty silent onlookers.

Six months later we received a letter from Fairbanks, Alaska, describing my ex-colleague's excitement at the role being played in his university research by the 'Year 8 syndrome,' which, he argued, made sense of living in the darkness and wilderness of central Alaska. 'Thank you, Year 8,' he concluded. 'I couldn't have done it without you.'

Year 8, which was by now Year 9, responded to the letter with its usual fervour of unconcern.

'I believe it, Dan,' smiled Marcus. 'At Market Upabit we had quite a different response to one of our 'characters' on the staff. I will remember him for the rest of my days, as will hundreds of ex-pupil.

*****

Commander Henry Bow RN was his name. He was a retired Royal Navy Commander, appointed to teach Mathematics. He had been a young naval sub-lieutenant engineer on a submarine in the last months of the Second World War. He had continued his service for a further thirty years and then on retirement decided to train to teach mathematics.

His teaching of Maths turned out to be like no other: speed and distance taught with measuring equipment rescued from scrapped ships and submarines, models of torpedoes, intricate maps of islands and charts of oceans. Eleven- to sixteen-year-olds were required to measure angles needed for trajectories of shells or slow and fast submarine dives and to calculate the radius of turn in order to stalk enemy ships and plot the spread of blast and shock-wave from explosions They were all the stuff of the Commander's 'real mathematics'. I decided not to intervene at first, and then pupils, Maths staff, and parents all showed enthusiastic support and the interest in Maths and the rise in standards was so enormous that I had no alternative but to leave well alone.

But I did worry – about what would happen when Her Majesty's Inspectors arrived in town. Henry's Maths all seemed so different from speeds of trains, filling of supermarket baskets, and the size of aristocratic estates.

There came a time during the inspection week when I was unable to keep Henry and Maths Inspector apart any longer. The inspector, senior in rank and experienced in inspecting Maths, made his way to the back of Henry's class and lent forward, pen and paper poised, while Henry, uncompromising as ever, drew a battle area, placed 'friendly' and 'enemy' forces, and then got pupils to plot courses and likely crossing points, and calculate maximum distances and angles.

This lesson, like all his others, was punctuated with rapid anecdotal mathematical examples of fleets of ships, volumes of water displaced by battleships, velocity of shells from ships guns, and how far a frigate could sail without refuelling, with added tales of shelling enemy ships and rescuing merchant seamen from the water. His blend of quiet explanation, rising to a crescendo as the 'battle' unfolded, brought the classroom into the action and made the atmosphere electric, teacher reliving his past and pupils engrossed in the present. Each pupil responded in their own way to each tale of derring-do, and then remembered the principles they illustrated.

But all was not well. The inspector suddenly started to write rapid, copious notes the sound of the scribbling cut through Henry's story. The scratching of the pen was audible to all. Now, Henry was as tolerant as the next man, but he was not used to competition when he was explaining. He was, after all, a former captain of a warship. His pact with 'his ratings' – as his pupils liked to be called – was 'I speak, you listen.' He could see no reason why allowances should be made for anybody. He became more and more agitated as the inspector wrote ever more furiously. After a while one little girl at the front said with some trepidation, 'Excuse me, Sir, on the blackboard you have just made 2+2=5' (or some such mistake).

Henry paused, nodded at the small, brave girl in the front row, drew himself up to his full but diminutive height – which suited service in submarines – and wagged a reproving finger at the poor inspector, whose nose was by now deep into his large black file. Henry's finger shook, his lips quivered. Eventually he managed to find some words. 'It's all his fault, that man at the back. I am used to people paying attention to me and not writing letters to someone while I am talking. Please cease, Sir.'

The inspector, who was more used to deference than confrontation, looked up, startled, and closed his file with a bang. He was not at all sure what to do. By the time he had thought of a strategy Henry had moved on.

'Thank you, Sir. I am obliged. I always think it preferable to surrender than have another torpedo fired at you. You are very wise. Now, class, we will continue.'

All this only came to my attention when the inspector himself, by now highly amused by it all, and a little shamefaced, came and told him at lunchtime. 'I would like to meet and congratulate Mr Bow, if I may, Headmaster. I have never seen a sixty-year-old teacher with such a rapport with teenagers. His lesson was so interesting I tried to copy down some of his anecdotes. I may have overstepped the mark. I would like to tell him that he broke most of the rules of lesson preparation and execution.but who cares! He had me just as hooked as the kids. Extraordinary but brilliant!'

And so it was, that at the end of the school day the three of us, without the lead inspector knowing, shared a cup of tea, one of the school kitchen's butterfly cakes, and a good chat.

'What a nice man, very discerning,' said Henry as the inspector left.

Now that is how professional discussion and debate should be conducted.

END OF THE DAY

Shaping our Ends

'There is a divinity shapes our ends, Rough-hew them how we will.'
W Shakespeare, Hamlet

You may believe that your past, your present and your future life is ordained by a Divinity, an Almighty God or Gods, or a Guiding Spirit, or the Wheel of Fortune, or just maybe by your own actions and decisions.

All of that is in the realms of belief, hope and conviction. What is a racing certainty, a given fact, is that from the ages of around five- to eighteen-years-old, up to one-third of your life will have been determined by one person alone, often depicted as working in a small back room with a white board covered in a matrix of squares, or bent over a computer with a similar matrix. Whichever it is, the brow will be puckered and a sickly smile, even a triumphant leer, will hide the firm jaw and spoil the set chin.

The ghostly person is the School Timetabler – a Miss Terious or Mister Chance. He or she will keep their head down, drink copiously of tea and coffee, work long hours, make only occasional excursions from their actual or metaphorical cupboard in order to make tedious, inconvenient, but necessary contact with colleagues, and generally keep out of harm's way.

This cubby-holed substitute for the Almighty or Spirit or Destiny will make key decisions about your life: what you will be doing, where you will be doing it, how long you will be doing it for, with whom you will be doing it, and who will oversee your doing of it.

All these will be ordained. You, the ultimate subject to the routine of the daytime life that will be laid down for you, will have no say in what the experience will be – until the moment you are actually subjected to the regime. Then you – whether you are the teacher or the taught – are free to make of it what you will. This is the way it is.

It is, I suppose, the nearest a mere mortal can get to divine power. So mused Anne-Marie Martial, the new Principal of Market Upabit Academy. She had only been the head of the academy for the past year but she considered herself already to be a veteran of the annual 'Timetable Rodeo', the inevitable cavalcade of the perennially suspicious, disgruntled, argumentative and disruptive. And yet, like most headteachers, she did not undertake the primordial task herself. Far too risky. It was a gateway to sycophancy, patronage, bribery, dubious practices, breaking of hearts; these were not matters that a Headteacher should be associated with, well, not obviously anyway.

These are dangers that any self-respecting, or plain wily, Head should steer well clear of – she was quite certain about that. Far better to create the image of being simply the font of power when all plaudits for a job well done would be put down to sound leadership and management, and all mistakes and disappointments attributed to incompetent underlings. Taking praise and diverting criticism are marks of the successful manager, or so her musings continued.

It followed that from the moment she took on the leading role at Market Upabit she delegated all management of the timetable to one of the Vice-Principals, Reg 'the Hedge' Hope, who had thrived on a reputation for stonewalling and brick-walling. 'They shall not pass', was Reg's motto, neatly encapsulated in the notice on his cubby-hole door: 'If the Door is Shut I am Not Here'. It was rarely open.

It was not that Anne-Marie was unsympathetic to her colleagues' worries and bitchings when she deemed them genuine. But from experience she knew that all too often the staff concerns were simply self-induced longings for an easier life, for a past, calmer, more compliant world that never actually existed. She saw this posture as unbecoming of professionals and would not be party to it. The trick was how to make them content without actually changing anything.

How to promote the philosophy of Voltaire's Doctor Pangloss: 'All is for the best in the best of possible worlds'?

She had done her stint as timetabler in another school. She knew the ropes and the knots in the ropes. She was, therefore, quite content to offer guidance and advice to colleagues aggrieved by the effects of the timetable, so long as she remained free from actual blame, or the obligation to do something about it. That was the challenge each summer, as the publication of next year's timetable grew closer.

This summer was like any other. The timetable preliminaries had been determined in outline between January and Easter. Heads of Departments had submitted their requirements for teaching groups, assumptions had been made about likely new full-time and part-time staff, and oddities, like the absolute necessity for Biology's Mrs Bloggs to pick up her son at the primary school at 3.30pm every Wednesday because of the au pair's contract, had all been taken account of.

Principal Anne-Marie, after the due few seconds of consultation with Reg, decided – as was traditional and therefore expected – that it was less nerve-wracking for her to have the draft timetable published just a week before the end of term. Intense nerve-wracking was always preferable to long, exhausting slow-burn wracking.

The period immediately after publication has been described as akin to the four-minute warning victims will get between the launch of a nuclear missile, the period of calm, and then the impact. It certainly felt that way to Anne-Marie. Hence, she ensured that the drafts were in staff pigeon-holes and transferred to personal computers a few minutes before the end of Friday afternoon. She was then able to enjoy a Saturday of village cricket and a Sunday family outing before sitting in her room at 7.30am on the Monday of the final week.

The ensuing timetable of 'Schedule of Staff Consultations' was not laid down but was predictable: it happened every year.

7.30am Peace and repose
7.45am Start of fall-out

239

Greta was first in. 'Ah! Principal. I didn't expect to find you in, but as you are, would it be convenient to have a short word?'

Same time, same greeting – every summer. Anne-Marie had been told to expect that and it had come to pass. This opening salvo came after Greta had already sat herself down and before Anne-Marie had indicated whether it was OK or not. Everything normal then, but she knew that was the way it would be.

'Now, Principal. Let me be honest. I am not at all happy about my next year's timetable. I have noted that Mrs Standing has been granted Wednesday afternoon off yet again. I have asked for Tuesday afternoon free, but it is not. It seems a small request after all my years of service. Can I assume you will do something about it?'

'Well, Greta. I am sorry you feel hard done by but I was not aware you had asked for time off on a Tuesday. When did you submit your request?'

'Goodness me, Principal, you do not expect me to have submitted a formal request to you, do you? I have spoken to Mr Hope. That should be sufficient, surely? You are far too busy, I assumed. And I am, after all, the longest serving member of staff. That should mean something.'

'Greta, we ask for formal requests so that we can assess all the competing claims and take account of special interests. You know that. You also know we receive quite a lot of similar requests. I am sorry that you failed to register your claim.'

Greta stood. 'I am not an unforgiving person, Principal. Your predecessor will no doubt have indicated that to you. I acknowledge your sorrow and accept your apology. Now, would you please register my request and tell the timetabler to get on with it.'

Anne-Marie started to raise a hand. But Greta was already making for the door. Anne-Marie just had time to shout after her before the door was firmly pulled to. 'I'll speak to Reg and ask him to contact you.' She did not know whether Greta had heard her, or even tried to, but she made a hasty note to ask Reg to see her. It was the start of her 'Notes for Reg'.

8.00am: Knocking on Anne-Marie's door. She looked up to find Hayden of History poking his head round the door. 'Just a quick word, Principal. Won't take long. It's about next year's timetable.'

Anne-Marie waved him into a chair. 'What is it, Hayden? (As if she did not know!)

'It's like this, Principal. Next year's timetable. I seem to have been put down to take 4C on a Friday afternoon for Personal and Social Education. Can't be done. Can't be done – it really can't. I've already been off this term with stress after taking 3C on a Monday morning for History and 5G on a Wednesday after lunch for PSE.'

He paused and so did Anne-Marie. There was nothing to say, really. She knew that she herself, one Vice-Principal, two Assistant Principals, the Head of Department and umpteen behind-the-scenes psychiatric mentors would continue for a further year to steer this rather brilliant but neurotic teacher through his nightmares of Main School teaching and at the same time ensure that he got as much Sixth Form teaching as could be reasonably provided. His Sixth Form examination results were sensational; the number wanting to take History breath-taking; the number going on to university legendary. Ways and means had to be found to keep him going.

At the moment he had built up a fresh speed. 'Principal, it is tantamount to a sentence of hard labour to ask me to take PSE lessons. I should be taking the A classes. There is no-one as good as me at it.'

Not exactly true, but no point in arguing. Anne-Marie allowed a silence to settle over the conversation. What she had to do was balance his needs and desires with the legitimate claims of his History colleagues, or there would be all hell to pay in the History department! And she was sure they had got the balance right.

'Look, Hayden, just rest assured that we will reconsider your timetable and continue to support your efforts – as the

241

school has always done. My door will always be open to you, if you want a further talk. Just have a relaxing holiday.'

'Thank you, Principal. You are always so reassuring.' Hayden had had his say. He was content. Anne-Marie made another note, 'Speak to Reg about Hayden. DO SOMETHING!!!' Then she added 'BIG M' which was the secret code she and Reg used to indicate to one another that this one really did have to be sorted. 'Before I Go Mad' was used sparingly but taken seriously.

8.15am: She had hardly pushed aside her memo when the door burst open. Nothing so gentlemanly as a knock. Six foot six inches of Phil the Hill stood in the doorway, with fingers tucked into his belt, looking for all the world like a Wild West gangster entering the Deadwood saloon. He, metaphorically, tipped back his Stetson and addressed Anne-Marie in what he habitually called his 'no-nonsense terms', but which Anne-Marie and colleagues called 'bloody rude'.

She thought of asking him to step back and enter again but decided in a split second that she probably had the upper-hand in this conversation. So she just leaned back in her swivel chair and rotated it a smidgen away from him. He was in full swing.

'What's all this I hear about me teaching the same Year 10 group twice in the same day? It's ridiculous. I take it you know about it.' Phil stayed in the doorway. Anne-Marie decided to leave him there. She knew she had the answer. There was more than a little satisfaction in feeling smug sometimes.

'Well, we simply acted on the information you gave us, Phil. You told us you could only come in three days a week next year and you take Year 10 for four lessons.' She paused while it sank in. Then she swivelled towards him and raised her eyebrows. Words, she thought, were superfluous.

Phil shuffled, and puckered his brow. He appeared to be still working it out. He looked up and stared censoriously at her. 'I assumed you managers were the experts at curriculum planning and timetabling. Surely it is not beyond the wit of man – or woman,' (he added hastily) 'to put this right?'

'Well, Phil, we could put it right by giving your group to someone else and reducing your hours accordingly. Would that be agreeable?' She knew very well it would not, unless Phil could increase his hours at the FE College, unlikely at this time of the year but she did not actually mind. She knew Reg the Hedge had some hours in hand from other part-timers. The ball was now firmly in Phil's court.

'All right, Principal I will accept it this once, but I will expect better next year.'

'Of course, Phil. We all want to improve don't we? I guarantee Reg and I will give your status the utmost further consideration next year.'

As Phil turned on his heel, Anne-Marie added another 'Note to Reg': 'Phil: NAR'. No Action Required. Very satisfying.

She managed to weather three more short confrontations before assembly time. First, a suggested timetable swop by part-timer, Cynthia, that would have meant co-part-timer, Pauline, having to stay in school all day, taking Period 1 and then Period 7 – a daft idea, but one which Cynthia defended by suggesting, somewhat petulantly, that Pauline could learn to knit, couldn't she?

Then, 'just a suggestion,' from Dick that he was better qualified to take the top group of geographers than Ali – a suggestion easily waved aside. Finally, a plea from lovelorn Launcelot to teach next-door to the delectable Guinevere – slightly more difficult to dismiss instantly since Anne-Marie knew that Ginny wanted to be as far away from Lance as possible. There was time to add to her 'Notes for Reg' and then off to morning assembly and a bit of school ritual of quite another dimension.

At the end of morning assembly Anne-Marie waylaid Reg. 'Here you are, Reg, just half a dozen timetable notes this year. Let me have your considered views in due course.'

Reg took them and thrust them into his pocket. 'Too busy with personal issues this week, Principal. Here you are – here are the answers.' He took a single sheet out of his other pocket and handed it over. Anne-Marie looked at the paper, and then at Reg incredulously.

'But you haven't looked at the questions yet.'

'Come on, Principal. I don't need to! They are just the same as last year and year before, and year before that. They are last year's questions so, here are last year's answers. They all start: "Dear XXXX, I have discussed your problem with Mr Hope at great length and find, with regret, that …". Easy peasy!' He paused and smiled at Anne-Marie, still standing open-mouthed. 'Just put them into pigeon-holes next Friday morning just before final assembly as usual. Then off you go and enjoy your summer break, Principal, as usual. You'll find it will all be forgotten when we return – as usual!'

Just a Little Matter

The final week had passed by. Last day of the school year at Market Upabit Academy: farewell school assembly; tutor group parties; mini-games on the field in glorious sunshine. Oh, and the final visits to bend the Head's ear from staff perennially 'not happy, Principal, not happy at all with next year's timetable.'

8.25am: Two more already done and dusted. Surely time for one more? Ah, yes, Caroline: in her thirties, wanting to be back in her twenties and looking as though she was in her forties. Chameleon Caro. Anne-Marie Martial had been warned – no real problems, but craving attention. Caroline peered round the door.

'Do sit down, Caroline, and what can I do for you?'

Caro pulled the chair right up against the Principal's desk, barely half a metre from Anne-Marie's inquisitive gaze.

'It is rather tricky, Principal, a bit embarrassing, and I must ask that you keep it confidential.'

'I can't give you that guarantee, Caroline, until I know what it is, so spill it out. We haven't got much time.' Anne-Marie had been warned not to prevaricate with Caro.

Caroline cleared her throat.

'Er, well, Principal, I have to tell you that I might be, well … err … compromised … err … pregnant …' she tailed off. Anne-Marie could understand why that might be. Caroline was not married and was known to have a London bus arrangement with boyfriends – either none or three at a time. Anne-Marie was not aware of the present arrival and departure schedule.

'Congratulations are in order, I hope, Caroline? it sounds like great news. Is it?' She wanted to sound as upbeat as possible.

'Well, er, it might be or it might not.' Caroline tailed off and she peered into the distance over Anne-Marie's shoulder, as though the answer might be out there somewhere.

Anne-Marie broke the silence. 'Well, it doesn't seem like a school timetable problem, Caroline. Perhaps we should—'

'Oh, but it is, Principal. Or might be.'

Silence again.

'Yes? Meaning what exactly?'

'You see the father might be Mr Hope, the timetabler!'

Anne-Marie could not help herself. 'What! Reg Hope! Crikey ...'

Silently to herself, Anne-Marie thought how on earth did weedy Reg manage that? Reg with a wife of thirty years and two sons at university. Blimey – was she hallucinating?

'You mean Reg Hope and you ...'

'Ye-e-e-s!' It came out rather sheepishly. 'At the end-of-term staff party in his little cubby-hole. He keeps a bottle of whisky in his filing cabinet you see, says it does wonders for the timetable. Well, it did wonders for me – I needed to have a lie down on his little desk.'

Was everything 'little' with Caroline? thought Anne-Marie.

There was a moment of silence again. This was no longer a 'normal' timetable conversation; care was needed.

'Caroline you said Reg *might* be the father – is there someone else?'

Caro cleared her throat again.

'Well, Eddie from Science was at the same party.'

'Oh dear, and did he also have whisky in the Science Preparation Room?

'Oh no.

'Thank goodness for that.'

'It was gin.'

'Gin! And at the same party?'

'Yes, he keeps a few bottles in the cupboard marked 'Private. Medicine Chest. For Staff Use Only' and he had a little desk as well.'

'Good Lord!' Anne-Marie wiped her brow. She thought she had better move the conversation on. She was learning more than she could cope with five minutes before morning assembly.

'Look, Caroline, we need to discuss this further.'

'And there is another possibility, Principal,' Caroline cut in, fearful that not all would be revealed when she really wanted to unburden herself.

'Not another member of staff at the same party?' Anne-Marie felt both aghast and admiring.

'Oh, no nothing like that. it's just that it might simply be a sort of prolonged indigestion – the doctor said it could be psychosomatic and I don't know what to think.'

Anne-Marie put her hand up. 'Hang on! Let's get this straight. Are you informing me, officially, that you may, or may not, have suffered, let us say, some physical change somewhere on the spectrum between immaculate conception, a rumbling tummy, rape, and a rather stimulating dream?'

'I don't know, Principal it might be none of those! I shan't know the true situation till the end of the school holidays, but I did come about next year's timetable. I needed you to know why I am asking to be moved out of the room next to Reg's next year! And as far away as possible from Eddy, too. It would be far too embarrassing, and I dare not ask Reg. I'd have to explain about Eddy.'

Anne-Marie let out a long breath and shook her head. She could cope with the room bit – once she had time to breathe. The implications of all the rest of the revelation would have to wait.

'I haven't done anything wrong, have I?' asked Caroline plaintively.

'Wrong?' thought Anne-Marie. 'What is *wrong*?' But then she shook her head. Now was not the time for existentialist musing on right and wrong – there was the question of the misuse of school desk and table, whatever their size, which was of course a potential disciplinary matter – but best keep away from trifles like that.

'Consider it done, Caroline. I'll get the rooms changed. Go away and, er, enjoy your break. Your health and, er, possibly the health of the baby, are paramount. Let me know exactly what the situation is once you know yourself! You realise there may be some, er, implications, but on the other hand, there might not. I prefer to deal with the real and the actual myself.'

'Thank you so much, Principal. I knew you would understand and sympathise.' Caroline slipped away, leaving Anne-Marie staring at the door. She looked at her watch. Two minutes to morning assembly. She picked up the internal phone.

'Reg, you seem to have got your subjects, timings, teachers and possibly periods,' she added as an afterthought, 'all muddled up. We need to sort them out soon.'

'Okay Principal, I shall look forward to that.'

Anne-Marie put the phone down. 'I doubt it, Reg,' she mused. 'I doubt it very much.'

Glittering Prizes

Miss Edith Flutter loved the annual prize-giving evening. It not only gave her the chance to show off the school and celebrate pupils' successes – that went without saying – but it was also the opportunity to demonstrate each year her own personal and unique qualities as a manager, organiser, administrator, friend of pupils, adviser of parents, leader of teachers and 'others'. An all-round good egg. A Headmistress (not Headteacher as was the modern, coarse appellation) to be reckoned with, and, who knows, even to be honoured.

That was not an idle thought. With a former Lord Justice of Appeal, former Secretary of State, former Ambassador, and former Permanent Secretary at some ministry or other as trustees, and a Dowager Duchess as Patron, there should be sufficient clout knocking about.

The only slight concern was the 'former' bit. Would any of the present-day government decision-makers (by which she meant honours and distinction decision-makers) remember who these old fogies were? Would a Dowager Duchess from Muckleton and assorted 'formers' count for much in the corridors of Westminster? Well, no use worrying about that. If she performed well in public tonight, her twenty-fifth appearance at the school's glittering prize-giving ceremony, it would do her no harm. It might make it easier for the idea of honouring 'our leader' to occur to at least one of that doddery but quite useful lot.

And then there was her carefully chosen guest speaker and prize-giver himself. The Lord Bishop. He was, after all, himself a member of the House of Lords, a force to be reckoned with. And what is most satisfactory, she reckoned, he is sympathetic to the current ruling party and a personal friend of the Prime Minister. He had once been the incumbent vicar at the Prime Minister's village church – and not many people knew that. Her Bursar and Business Manager, Bartholomew Showall, had researched that precious detail, and at the same time unearthed a priceless additional nugget: as a curate, the Bishop had assisted at the Prime Minister's christening. That must surely count. Well done, Bart, and well done, Bishop.

All very good reasons for persuading the trustees to invite him to make the presentations – not that they had much choice. She had not held down the post of Head for twenty-five years without knowing how to get her way with the governing board – on the important issues anyway. And once the Dowager had greeted the proposal with a rumbustious cry of, 'Old Bishop Cedric, eh? He'll do well enough. He's one of us, is Cedric. Sound man. Spouts too much Bible for my liking but he won't alarm the parents. those that stay awake that is, because they won't understand him!' She chortled at her own witticism. Her fellow trustees had joined in.

At first the school Chaplain, the Reverend Oscar Oliphant, was supportive. 'A good choice, Edith. My Lord Bishop intones a moving blessing at the close of events.'

'No, no, Oscar. I haven't invited him just to bless us all. I have asked him to dole out the prizes and give an address.'

There was a pregnant pause while the chaplain rocked back and forth and contemplated his reply.

'I see, I see, well that is brave, Edith, very courageous, I may say.' He cleared his throat. 'You do know his reputation as a speaker, I assume.'

'Yes, I know there is a bit of a downside, Oscar. The Bishop is well known for going off-script. I gather he wanders into epistemological realms where few can, or want to, follow.'

Oscar raised his eyebrows. 'Edith, that is a gracious way of putting it! If the Lord Bishop gets the opportunity to muse on the distinction between justified belief and unsubstantiated personal opinion, or to launch himself into interpretations of epiphany or the concept of resurrection, there'll be no stopping him, I'm afraid, irrespective of the relevance to the audience.' Oscar paused again to clear his throat. 'Have you heard what he did last week?'

'No, enlighten me, Oscar.' A tiny tremor of trepidation ran through Edith's body at this point.

'Well, My Lord Bishop was invited to speak at a national conference of midwives and spoke for an hour on conflicting theories of the Immaculate Conception.'

Edith gulped. 'Well, I suppose that's all right if they were expecting it.'

Oscar sighed. 'They were not. His contribution had been advertised as an account of the Bishop's youthful evangelical adventures in the Congo. It seems that a lot of midwives contemplate doing good work in Africa at some point in their careers. He was supposed to be an inspiration to them. By all reports I don't think he was. So you see why I am not as enthusiastic about your choice as you might have hoped. There is no knowing what funny ideas our pupils and parents will be going home with.'

'I understand, Oscar. But the deed is done now. I have briefed him personally on what is expected and how long he can speak. I have given him just eight minutes on the grounds that we must get the pupils and families home in good time. I am sure he understands that.' Oscar made no immediate reply. Edith carried on, 'I know I can rely on your support to rein him in, dear Oscar.'

On the great evening – 'Glittering Prizes Day' as the Dowager habitually called it – trustees, senior staff and guests were assembled in the Head's study, while parents and pupils jostled in the main hall.

'Comforting to know that some things never change,' the Lord of Appeal was saying to his fellow trustee, Cuthbert Hall, ex-top Civil Servant, as they both balanced their plastic plates and glasses in the time-honoured tradition of British institutional receptions. 'Tuna and lettuce sandwiches and sweet sherry again. All's well with the world, eh Cuthbert?'

'Mmmmmm,' replied Cuthbert, 'but look on the bright side, my Lord. I note it is Spanish sherry this year, or a choice of a glass of chilled elderflower sparkling wine. For the past ten years it has been that ersatz British sherry and warm

251

elderflower cordial. So, things are looking up in Edith's last years, it seems.'

There was a loud clap of hands. Edith was taking charge.

'Time to go,' announced Edith in a commanding voice. With a quick glance at her watch, she had broken off from a somewhat tedious discussion about school finances with her favourite governor, Sir Maurice Denley, Chairman of a large retail consortium.

'Could you all follow the Duchess and my Lord Bishop, and me,' she announced. At that precise moment the door opened, and a small, pinched face peered timorously around the crowded room.

'What is it, Miss Broad?' Edith Flutter's peremptory question left no doubt of her irritation at the untimely interruption.

'I've brought your remote mike, Headmistress. I I thought it was easier to fix it here rather than on the stage, but if —' Sybil Broad, Head of IT, was not used to speaking while being observed by such an august company of distinguished guests.

'My what?' cut in Edith.

'You remember, Headmistress. You agreed last week to use our new remote public address system. I have to attach the remote microphone to you. It leaves the Bishop free to use the microphone on the stand at the corner of the stage if you remember?' Her voice began to trail away. 'The Duchess has the usual table microphone in front of her with the wire to the system.' At this Sybil came to a complete halt and looked appealingly at her Headmistress.

Edith now recalled a short conversation with Head of IT Sybil – en passant – as she had swept through the IT department a week ago. She had not really understood what Sybil was getting at. Now it was becoming clear. She would have liked to brush Sybil aside with some devastatingly managerial gesture, but her guests had gone silent and were watching the confrontation with interest. Leadership had to be shown.

'Of course, Miss Broad, what does it entail?'

'I just need to clip this mike to your blouse, Headmistress.' Sybil waved the object in the air.

'On my blouse!' cried Edith, putting her hand to her mouth. 'I do not really want such a thing pulling on my blouse.' Edith had taken a long time choosing a crisp orange frilly blouse to go with her royal blue jacket and matching skirt. It would not do at all to have an alien gubbins spoiling the effect.

'Well, it could be attached to your skirt, Headmistress. It wouldn't be seen under the table. And it is a powerful microphone. It will easily pick up your voice.'

Edith contemplated this latest twist. 'All right. That seems satisfactory. Fix it, then.'

Sybil clipped it onto the outside of the skirt in a trice. Edith discovered that her academic gown covered it nicely. Excellent. All was now ready for the off.

'Come now, Your Graces,' she addressed the Dowager Duchess and Bishop. 'Time to go. Tenth time for you, isn't it, Duchess? Only fifteen more to catch up with the late Duke.' She attempted to be bright and cheery.

Edith led the cohort in file towards the double doors at the rear of the school hall. The doors would swing open miraculously when they were a yard away. That had been the job of the outgoing Head Girl and Deputy Head Girl for as long as anyone could remember. The girls could watch the progress of the parade as it approached via a small clear window in the door. It worked like clockwork every year.

It was just unfortunate that the incident with the fitting of the microphone had left the Duchess long enough to put away a final sherry and, being now light-headed as well as light-hearted, she leaped in front of Edith in the last yard before reaching the door. Crying, 'My turn, Headmistress,' she flung herself at the double doors. They did not budge. For a split second one of the gracious flowers of England was spread-eagled across the doors, before shaking her head like a yellowhammer who has flown into a patio window and falling backwards into the bosom of the Bishop -- who had no choice but to catch her, so fast was her rebound.

There were general gasps all round, but no real concern as the Duchess recovered immediately and waved away all offers of help.

'Who did that?' the Duchess was heard to mutter as she struggled free from the Bishop's embrace. 'Who has changed the doors, eh?'

'No-one has changed the doors, Your Grace,' said Edith as gently as she could. 'They have been opening this way for the past one hundred years, since your grandfather presented them. And that is why the girls have been stationed to open them, for the past one hundred years.'

'Well, someone should have reminded me,' replied the Duchess irritably. 'I can't be expected to remember everything.'

'Let's get you on your feet, Your Grace. The show must go on,' said Edith as she hauled the Dowager upright. 'But perhaps you had better sit this one out.'

'Certainly not!' cried her Grace. 'The Duke and I survived the 1940s Blitz as children, you understand I shall not, repeat *not* be put out of action by a pair of anti-social wooden doors!

Get me a glass of water on stage and I will show you what the Muckletons are made of.' She wagged her finger at the Head Girl, who cried, 'Oh Lord,' and made for the stage to check the water.

Edith could see that there was no point in arguing. She shrugged her shoulders; the Dowager dusted herself down; the official crocodile shook itself out. All were poised once again for the grand entrance. This time Edith made no mistake. She strode forward purposefully in the vanguard, nodding vigorously to Hetty Plowright, the Head of Music, far down the Hall. This was a signal for the school orchestra to strike up. A drum roll and crashing cymbals brought the audience to its feet with a start and made Edith blink in astonishment. She had forbidden Head of Music to play the Grand March from Verdi's *Aida*, requesting 'something a little less ostentatious', and now she found the audience rising to its feet to the unmistakable first bars of the Entry of the Toreadors from Bizet's *Carmen*. And, what is more, most of the parents and pupils were joining in the thumping 'Tee-tee-tee-tum-ta -ummty-tummty-tee' with obvious gusto. The only thing to do to keep any semblance of dignity was to get to the stage as quickly as possible. A suitable conversation with Hetty could wait. Edith upped the pace, striding down the central aisle until halfway down she realised that no-one else was following her.

She spun round and there, back near the entrance, was the Dowager Duchess of Muckleton hand-in-hand with My Lord Bishop, flitting from side to side shaking hands with members of the audience, in the manner of a royal walk-about. The Duchess was not only offering her hand to be shaken but offering the Bishop's hand, too.

'Go on, Cedric. Give her a peck!' she cried when the Bishop was shaking a young mother's hand rather vigorously.

'O, goodness me! Do you think so?' said the Bishop. He was thoroughly enjoying himself, relishing the unusual attention. He was saved from making a momentous social decision by being pulled across the aisle by the Duchess who had spotted one of her estate workers.

Further down the aisle Edith was standing metaphorically scratching her head.

Right by her sat Mrs Penelope Morgan. She had remained sitting because she was bouncing three-year-old Patsy on her knee. Patsy bent her head and peered behind following the Headmistress's gaze. Just at that moment the Duchess had lifted her silver cane in the air in some triumphal gesture, carrying her diaphanous olive-green cloak upwards. Now, with her six-foot outstretched green wingspan and little yellow cap she looked for all the world like a giant Jurassic Park parrot poised to strike a prey. Patsy's eyes opened wide.

'A Terror Dactyl!' cried the little girl, throwing herself against her mother's chest. She snuggled under mum's coat.

That was the last straw for Edith. She strode back down the aisle and grasped the Dowager's hand, hauling her and the handcuffed Bishop down the aisle. The Dowager wouldn't let the Bishop go, so all three set off for the stage in a series of short bursts like a sort of advanced hopscotch.

Meanwhile the school orchestra stuck up with a third repetition of the Entry of the Toreadors. Conductor Hetty's arms pumped up and down and little second former Betty Timmis banged heartily on the timpani. By the time the stage party had sorted themselves out on stage the Toreadors' March was into its fifth *da capo*.

The problem was that none of the special guests could remember the seating plan displayed in the Head's study. And so, there was much peering at name cards on the chairs, jostling for position and cries of:

'I think you are here, Jane.'

'Let's move the cards, Cuthbert and we will be able to sit together.'

'Can anyone see where I am seated?'

'This is a rum do.'

'Over here, Colonel.'

Edith leaned on the table and stared forward towards the audience – who were still standing dutifully, and still humming the Toreadors' March albeit with decreasing gusto.

Edith was in no mind to get involved with the minor mayhem behind her. Next to her the Duchess took her seat, totally oblivious of any hiatus. Finally, at Edith's request, the Duchess bellowed, 'Good evening!' into her microphone, before taking a large sheaf of papers from her olive-green handbag which dangled from a chain at her waist.

'Just a short welcome from me,' she growled, leaning into the mouthpiece.

Edith, the trustees, the staff and those parents and pupils who had attended previously knew very well that it would not be 'short', but they also knew that they could do nothing about it. The Duchess claimed that the parents expected 'a proper welcome'. And whether they did, or not, they got one.

She kept them standing for a full minute while she greeted – in her gruff, upper-upper-class tone – 'My Lord Bishop, noble guests, distinguished visitors, ladies, gentlemen, our excellent pupils, and any "others" I have missed.' It was an annual ritual – a delight for her and a chore for the audience. It had to be endured. But tonight, things were slightly different, producing a small murmur of unusual interest in what was going on. Her Grace had not switched on the table microphone, and despite Sybil Broad's frantic efforts at the console in the wings, her remarks went unheard beyond the orchestra at the front. Nobody commented, nobody complained. Indeed, there was a contented sigh of relief, if anything.

'You may sit,' said the Duchess, eventually waving her left hand vaguely over her head.

'Now they know who's boss,' she muttered to the chief guest, leaning confidentially towards the Bishop. The Bishop, being occupied with sorting out his bundle of speech papers, did not catch her last observation. The rest of the audience did – because at that precise moment Sybil had mastered the volume control. As the Duchess sat down, her voice came into the range of Edith's remote mike. Her ducal claim to mastery of the night's proceedings boomed out over the tannoy. The Duchess could see people looking at each other but had no idea why. Edith immediately looked down at her mike but had no idea how to turn the sound down. She looked round for Sybil Broad. She was nowhere to be seen. The murmur in the audience grew to a buzz.

'Now is the time to *carpe* the *diem*,' Edith decided. 'Take over, Edith,' she told herself, 'before her Grace gets into her stride.' She knew there would be no stopping her Grace once she got into caustic asides mode. She had even been rebuked as a young Countess at Queen Elizabeth's coronation in 1953. If she wanted to say something, she would.

Edith stood up quickly with her 'Headmistress's Report'. Polite applause rose from the floor, initiated, on her instructions, by loyal bursar, Bartholomew, seated at the back of the hall. It was taken up by the rest of the audience expressing some light relief.

'Your Grace, Lord Bishop, Lord Justice, lords, ladies and gentlemen, good evening.'

'WE ARE IN FOR THE LONG HAUL HERE, CEDRIC.' The Dowager's voice crackled out of the loudspeakers once again. Most of the audience, as well as the Bishop, did not pick it up, but some did, and Edith, who had heard all of it, could detect a little ripple of laughter in the hall.

She gritted her teeth and ploughed on. There was nothing else for it. She praised the girls, their teachers, the excellent examination results, the sporting successes and gave out some well-chosen, notable statistics. Warming to the task, Edith felt in her element. Maybe the previous hiatus could be forgotten. She was just about to move on to equally selective and impressive facts about sports results when 'the voice' cut in again.

'NOT VERY ORIGINAL, BISHOP, BUT IT'S WHAT THEY WANT TO HEAR.' The Duchess's mutterings in the direction of the Bishop were audible to all, even Edith. Sybil Broad, in an attempt to raise the level of the Headmistress's audibility and over-ride the Duchess, had instead succeeded in booming out the Duchess's remark at maximum decibels to everyone. Luckily Sybil, white-faced and in a state of panic was standing by the mixer and able to switch off the sound after the word

'Bishop'. Only the front rows, and the guests on the stage could hear the whole sentence.

'Could be the most interesting prize day we have ever attended, eh My Lord?' murmured Cuthbert Hall to the judge.

'Might even be the first one I have ever managed to stay awake through,' replied his Lordship.

Edith was rummaging through her notes and made a snap decision based on what was happening on the front line. She looked up from her papers and addressed the audience.

'Now, you will probably know that at this point I usually congratulate all the girls who have produced so many excellent sports results, and the staff who coached them, and then have, in the past, described the excellence of all the clubs and societies and extra-mural activities that this school offers all girls, but tonight I am not going to do that. I know you are all waiting eagerly for the Bishop's address.'

She paused at this point, praying that Bartholomew Showall would pick up the cue.

'Go on, Bart, do it,' she growled to herself.

He did. There came from the back of the hall a single clap followed, Lord be praised, by a few more and then a dutiful hall-full of polite applause. Few of the parents knew what they were clapping for – the shortening of the Headmistress's report or the anticipation of a longer Bishop's address, but they clapped all the same. Edith nodded to the audience but hoped Bartholomew would recognise it was for him. His salary rise was secure.

'And so,' she continued, 'without more ado I will hand you over to our eminent guest speaker.'

'AND PRE-EMINENT BORE,' came over the airwaves. Edith's remote mike was doing its job unfortunately.

Edith's jaw dropped. She had to do something – quickly – or the Duchess's continuing interventions would become even more outrageous and, what was even worse, make her, Edith, a laughing stock.

She gestured to the Bishop to move to the microphone at the front of the stage. At almost the same time she pushed the remote mike down the inside of her skirt. She felt its coldness between her bloomers and bare tummy – not quite where she wanted it to end up, but it should silence the Duchess for good. She had no experience of alien objects in her knickers and hoped she could now just ignore it. She then made another snap managerial decision. She moved her chair away from the Duchess to the other side of the stage, hoping that parents and pupils would appreciate it was for the purpose of better hearing the Bishop.

The Bishop rose to polite applause and approached the microphone on the stand. Now a bit wary of microphones he tapped it twice lightly and stood back in case it exploded. Two little pops were clearly heard in the hall. That seemed satisfactory. Emboldened now, Bishop Cedric raised a hand and pronounced, 'Samuel 1: verse 10. After these signs take place —'

There was a low rumble over the airways – uuuuhhrmm. He looked around. Everyone was determined not to have heard anything. He noticed the Headmistress's gaping mouth but ploughed on, '… do what must be done.' A further rumble – aaaargh – ending in a distinct burp.

The Bishop did not panic, but Edith did. It was dawning on her now that the 'noises off' were the sounds of very irritated gastric juices – hers! The microphone down her skirt was picking up all the sounds of internal organs in disarray! Instinctively she pushed the mike further down her knickers, right down between her legs. She could feel the warm touch. She could also feel a growing menace in the back passage. She pressed her legs together.

'And the Lord will be with us,' intoned the Bishop. At which precise moment Edith gave up the unequal struggle and a low, deep, flatulent, ripping sound stole through the sound system and filled the hall.

There was no mistaking it. Edith was aghast. So was sound technician Sybil, who in a frantic attempt to deaden the rippling sound was turning all the knobs – to no avail. The microphone had a fixed volume control on the stand. Sybil was stranded, helpless. But undaunted she rushed onto the stage from behind the curtain, bending low as if believing that by stooping you could become invisible.

'It's Soppy Sybil,' cried one young unidentifiable first former, 'Go on, Miss, fix it!'

Sybil reached the mike stand and turned the volume down. She curtseyed to the Bishop, then curtseyed to the Duchess, and then to the audience, put her hand over her mouth and fled off-stage, all in a twinkling of an eye.

'Thank you, Miss.' The Bishop stopped. He realised that his voice now reached no-one. He had been rendered inaudible then speechless. He looked around wildly. Sybil rushed back on again, curtseying again to the Duchess, to the Headmistress, to the audience, all the way across the stage. At last she reached the Bishop, leaned across him, and switched the sound up again. Just as Edith's irritable bowel syndrome was reaching its zenith. The thunderclap reverberated round the Hall. Some mothers let out an audible gasp, recognising the symptoms. One dad shouted encouragingly at Sybil, 'Go it, lass. You're winning!'

Edith, stage left, thrust a hand down her skirt and yanked out the offending instrument, to thunderous applause, led by the Lord of Appeal, who was by now standing to get a better view of the best show in town. He gestured the whole stage party to stand and join in the applause.

The Dowager, who had not seen or heard any of the proceedings because she had fallen asleep as soon as the Bishop had stood to address the school, looked around puzzled, and deciding that the Bishop must have finished his speech, switched on her table microphone and cried, 'Jolly well said, Bishop. Excellent speech. Memorable. Do come and sit by me again.'

Meanwhile Edith strode off backstage, grabbed a mike and microphone stand and marched back on, plonking the stand at the front of the table with what she hoped would come across as a display of managerial superiority. She felt a wave of satisfaction. She was in charge again. She gestured the

261

Dowager to remain seated and for the rest of the stage party to resume their seats, too.

'My apologies, my Lord Bishop and your Grace. Modern technology, you know. These minor irritations do occur with new gadgets and we do have to proceed now with the evening's programme.'

The Bishop fully expected to be recalled to the mike and rustled his papers. But Edith was having none of it. She had told the old fool not to quote from the Bible but to recognise that over half the school's intake was now Muslim, Hindu, Buddhist or Jewish, and only a quarter were Church of England. He had been asked to deliver words that would respect them all, and he had failed. That was her view. He had had his chance and he had blown it.

'The Bishop has taken a great deal of trouble,' she said, 'to enlighten us, and his entire speech will shortly be printed in the school magazine alongside my report. You, and indeed all those unable to be here this evening, will be able to peruse it.'

Bartholomew was once again up to it. A ripple of claps developed into proper applause. 'Well done again, Bart,' she thought. Even higher salary perhaps!

The Bishop seemed resigned to his speech's fate, and to Edith's imperious decision.

'I will now ask the Bishop to distribute the prizes,' announced Edith, ignoring the Duchess who was about to do her own introductions. And now that the remote mikes were well away, no one but Edith could hear her Grace's muttered, 'Bloody woman!'

The Bishop and Edith arranged themselves in front of the table loaded with trophies and books. The Chaplain, the Very Reverend George Olliphant, took up his place beside the pile of cups, shields and books to hand the correct one to the Chief Guest, as he had done for the past twenty years. The Headmistress read out the list, as she, too had done for the past twenty-five years. The long, laborious ceremony of 'prize distribution', known to generations of school pupils, ground into action.

'The Muckleton Prize for Sport to Molly' and 'the Muckleton Prize for Science to Henry', and 'the Muckleton Prizes for Ancient this and Modern that and Doing this and Doing that' – all proceeded at solemn pace. Beaming recipients climbed on the stage right and descended left. Parents clapped and cheered enthusiastically. This is what they had come for. There was an air of time-honoured tradition returning to the evening.

The only fly in the ointment was the Bishop's insistence on asking each recipient what their favourite subject was or what career they were intending to follow. Thus, the ceremony, instead of proceeding at pace, dragged on.

At last it came to the final prize, 'The Muckleton Prize for Service to the Community'. This year it had been won by Sharon – not Ms Flutter's preferred recipient, but she had been assured that Sharon had been active in the local community and had been quite brilliant in the school play and the local amateur dramatics. Edith appreciated all that, but still harboured a nagging doubt about Sharon's motives and tactics.

But there we are, thought Edith, must be charitable. The staff had supported her nomination and here she was rising from her seat and walking like a seasoned model down the centre aisle to the platform. Edith noted that despite warning Sharon several times that the dress code was skirts one inch below the knees, Sharon's was one inch above, and the gap in her blouse was at least one inch longer than anyone else's, and the regulation platform shoes seemed to have grown a distinct heel. But  there was nothing Edith could do. The apparition was on its way. Sharon climbed the steps, turning heads both in the hall and on the platform.

She tripped lightly over to the Bishop, made a little curtsey thus exposing more cleavage, and took her book of poems.

'And what are you intending to do after school,' asked the Bishop.

Sharon paused, looked him straight in the face and fluttered her eyelids demurely.

'Well, my Lord' she replied, 'I *was* thinking of going straight home.' She fluttered her eyes again and flounced off the stage, looking back at the Bishop as she reached the steps. Unfortunately the conversation had taken place next to the microphone and was broadcast across the whole audience. Mothers' mouths opened, dads tried to suppress their giggles, the Lord of Appeal felt drawn to shouting 'Attagirl!' but restrained himself. The Dowager looked around wondering what was going on. Edith went pale and leaned on the table, thoughts of national honours thrust out of her mind. It was the Very Reverend Olliphant who saved the day. He leapt to the microphone, raised his hand in blessing, and in his best, most reverend voice intoned:

'Let us pray.'

Tricky Dicky

Having regaled his friends with the story of Edith and her prize-giving, Marcus wound up the evening at The Babbling Brook with this tale of a Head about to retire – not himself, he hastened to add, but a chap he knew in the next town.

This colleague was coming to the end of a distinguished career leading, for nigh on fifteen years, a school in the middle of a working-class district where staff, pupils and parents shared an enthusiasm for training pupils for trades, and particularly those trades that were plentiful in the steel industry.

Headteacher Richard had struggled, coped, and survived which was more than could be said of most of his teaching colleagues who tended to move out of the school almost as soon as they moved in. Jobs were plentiful, expectations high, tolerance, well, decidedly low. So, Richard had to live on his wits, to be one step ahead of both his staff and the kids and their parents. He invariably managed this because, unknown to them, he himself had been brought up in a similar environment. He surprised many a recalcitrant pupil by knowing exactly what they were getting up to.

A couple of boys might nip down to the end of the sports field for a quick fag only to find Richard leaning against a tree nonchalantly flicking flies with the walking stick he invariably sported out of doors. 'Hello, lads,' he would greet them cheerfully. 'Nature study? That's very gratifying. Come with me and we can identify some wildflowers together.' And that was their lunchtime done for.

'How did Tricky Dicky know we were coming here?' they would ask each other. 'Blowed if I know.'

On another occasion a larger boy, or indeed girl, might be about to bully a smaller one in the shadows of the outside toilet block when a metallic voice would boom out, 'Stop that, Kenny or Kimberley! And come straightaway to my office!' It was the Head through his loud hailer.

Eventually the school community learned that Richard Old had a powerful pair of binoculars and a very, very loud loudhailer, augmented in the course of time by infra-red traps, self-locking gates, and a bank of CCTV cameras. A safe place indeed but also a bit of a prison, which suited Richard down to the ground! Although staff and pupils eventually worked out where the cameras were and who was monitoring them, they never quite knew which were switched on and were active and which were dud!

Richard also had a passion for enhancing his school's private funds. He used ingenious methods. One scheme that ran for years involved buying old out-of-date window frames by the truckload and getting students on punishment duty to give them a lick of paint. He would then sell them as garden-frames to all the hundreds of allotment-holders in the town.

This little wheeze was complemented by a freezer service. His school 'Horticultural Club' (a necessary official cover for his enterprise) grew ordinary and exotic vegetables and fruit, many under the frames provided by the garden-frame business. These would be sold fresh and the excess chilled in the Food Technology facility and sold to staff and parents at considerable profit.

He even managed to extract a 'donation' from the new County Education Officer. This august gentleman had come to the school to meet the local town Heads and, as time drew on, he announced that he had to leave in the 'next twenty minutes' to get to the shops, as it was his wife's birthday and he had yet to buy a birthday present. In the twinkling of an eye Richard opened both flaps of his jacket, displaying a row of smart ladies' watches dangling from the right inside pocket and a range of necklaces dangling from the left-hand pocket. 'No need to go rushing off, chief,' said Dicky with a large winning smile. 'We have just what you need!' The CEO could not, and did not, decline.

And so, the school was always, in his time, 'cash-rich', and was more frequently painted and better refurbished than any other in the town. On top of that, youngsters from poorer households were provided with whatever bits of school uniform they needed. All very satisfactory, if unconventional. Dicky was also not averse to playing the odd trick on both members of staff and pupils. 'My little japes,' he called them. 'Keeps them on their toes!'

On one occasion he directed the school's Premises Manager to ring the fire alarm halfway through the dinner hour at one o'clock. Of course, there was utter chaos. All fire drills in the school's history had been carried out at reasonably convenient times like just before morning or afternoon breaks. No-one knew what to do in the dinner hour. No pupil or teacher was in a class, and as Dick discovered, some of his colleagues who had important marshalling jobs during an emergency were off down at a local pub. Only Richard himself seemed to be amused by the unannounced fire drill! But they took his point when he used the debacle to demonstrate that you could not choose when a fire started. The school now needed to work out a Plan B for break times. Point taken.

At another time he challenged the whole of the sixth form, two hundred students, to complete the school's cross-country six-mile run in under one hour. The route would be marked and policed by the PE Department, he assured them. A suitable prize would await all those who completed the course in under sixty minutes.

The whole of the 'Sixth' accepted the challenge. 'Easy-peasy,' they thought. They knew the senior course and knew that an even pace would crack it well under the hour mark.

Well, it would have done, except that Dicky had arranged with the PE staff to put up a barrier over the track on the four-mile mark with an arrow pointing to a different route, which, unbeknownst to the runners, would add an extra mile. Only a handful beat the one-hour target! They were incensed, of course, until they discovered as they arrived back that Tricky Dicky had provided at his own expense a prize for every one of them in a big Bran Tub on the finishing line. 'Mens sana in corpore sano,' was his excuse. 'A healthy mind comes from a healthy body. Just remember that next time I challenge you,' he warned them, 'you will give it long and careful thought, because I might not be showing my generous nature next time!' But Richard's biggest, most jaw-dropping 'jape' astounded all his colleagues and students.

After the singing of the hymn in senior assembly one Monday morning, he announced, 'Over the weekend my secretary Ms Marjorie Smyth-Harris and I got married. We also changed our name to "Potter" after the pub at the end of the school drive, The Jolly Potter'. With that he marched off-stage with a bouncy step and left the congregation of senior students and staff in gobsmacked silence. Those present that morning will never forget the sense of utter astonishment and pride that here was a Head utterly dedicated to the welfare of his school and all who sailed in her, but utterly fearless of public opinion tradition and convention.

Inevitably, of course, it all had to come to an end, but his retirement was at Richard's choosing. He did not 'retire' simply and quietly, of course. There were a series of retirement 'do's'. The Rotary Club marked his retirement, as the Drama Club had done the week before, the Golf Club would do so the following week, and the Old Students Association the day after. The final events would be a grand staff dinner on his last night in the profession and a tearful farewell to the school on the last day.

For the Rotary Club occasion, a veritable banquet, Richard had been allocated his own parking spot in the town square for his ancient Mercedes, right outside the restaurant door. His colleagues made sure the whole event was a fitting marker for a renowned member. A good time was had by all. At the end of the festivities Richard made his farewells and stepped out into the night.

It was only when he was attempting to drive away that his suspicions were aroused. The Merc was revving as pleasingly as normal but the car was not moving, and the revs started to turn into screeching noises until he eased off the accelerator. He switched off and got out. It was then that he saw the source of the problem. The car had no wheels! NO wheels! The Merc was propped up on four sets of bricks placed where the wheels should have been, and had been when first parked. Richard gaped and banged his fist on the roof. 'Typical of this place!' he growled. 'Brazen theft! Is there any place on earth as diabolical as this for open cynical crime?' He banged his hands down again in frustration. It might be locals, he thought, but it could be a gang from London or Birmingham or any other city. It's so easy to make a snatch and be miles away in half an hour.

There was no-one around. His Rotarian pals were still finishing their port. Then the club's President and Secretary appeared on their way to their cars. 'Hello, Dick, you still here?' said the President, surprised. And before Dick could answer he noticed the predicament. 'Oh Lor'. What have we here?'

'You may well ask, Bob. Car wheels gone! Just disappeared. In the middle of the town. Can you believe it?'

'All we can do is go with you to the police station just round the corner,' said Bob. 'Come on.'

'Right,' said Richard, 'let's get cracking.'

And so, Headmaster and Rotarian friends marched off in unison to the police station. They were greeted by the duty Sergeant, Sergeant Perks. He turned out to be a former pupil of Richard's school – and one whom Richard had often predicted would finish up in law, on one side or the other! Richard's heart sank a little when he saw the Sergeant's smile metamorphose into a smirk when he saw who had entered his precinct. But he brightened when the Sarge listened to the tale, clucking his tongue with exclamations of 'dear me, dear me'.

'Well, something's got to be done,' was the policeman's next response. Then he sucked his pencil before scratching his head with it.

'Tell you what, sir, I'll come back with you, and survey the scene, so that I can write a full report. And we had better make sure the car is still there, eh?' he laughed, apparently hoping to ease the tension. It did nothing to appease Dicky's anger and exasperation.

'Good idea, Perks,' said Dicky and set off for the door, followed by an entourage of Rotarian President, two Rotarian friends and Sergeant Perks. The quintet tripped back to the crime scene. As they reached the middle of the square Richard pointed out the car, and then his eyes widened, his pointing finger sagged and his steps slowed. So did his Rotarian colleagues.

'What on earth—' began Richard. The Merc was still there but so were the wheels! All four of them! And the whole car had been washed, waxed and polished!

'You say this is your car?' asked the Sergeant. 'The gleaming one with the four wheels?'

'Yes. Yes,' spluttered Richard. 'What's going on?' He looked round wildly.

Oh dear, oh dear,' said Perks stroking his chin. 'Seems to me you have been having too much of a good time, Mr Old ... er ... Potter. By rights I should breathalyse you now. I'm not sure you are fit to drive.'

'I've only had one beer,' sputtered Richard in a somewhat strangled voice. 'My friends here will vouch for that, won't you?' he pleaded.

'Well, I'm sure that these good folk will tell the truth and nothing but the truth, but I am still duty-bound to breathalyse you, you know, if I have any suspicion.'

'Surely you can't harbour any suspicions about your old Head now, can you?'

Richard was not sure whether that was a wise question. It went quite contrary to his long-held Headteacher's dictum that 'one should never ask a question to which one did not know the answer.' But Perks was in a jovial mood. In fact, he appeared to be relishing his old Head's discomfiture.

I'll tell you what, headmaster. I'll go quietly back to the station and erase all records of this encounter. Meanwhile, you and your Rotarian friends can sort it all out, eh? But I do advise that there is a taxi rank over there.'

'Just wait here, Dick,' said the President, 'while we go back inside and arrange transport for you and the car. We won't risk anything.'

His Rotarian pals disappeared back into the restaurant and Richard sensed movement all around him. Out of the shadows figures appeared, first Tom Margieson, the Head Boy, and then Helen Wright, Head Girl, then two more prefects and then dozens of sixth formers, all carrying spanners, washing buckets, wash leathers and polishing cloths. And then his Rotarian pals, the whole lot of them, appeared out of the restaurant, and then Perks reappeared from the direction of the police station. All were laughing their heads off. They were all in on the conspiracy.

Richard's jaw dropped. He gaped, gasped and then guffawed! 'You b******s, you little b******s, you utterly splendid and outrageous little b******s.'

'Yes,' said Helen Wright handing him a bucket and brush. 'You taught us well, Headmaster! You are not the only one who can dream up tricks, you see. Welcome to victim-land!'

Paradoxically, it was the most heart-warming send-off ever!

271

Acknowledgements

First of all, enormous thanks must go to Pat Rutterford and the trustees of the James Rutterford Trust for their enthusiastic embracing of the project and to Jenny Blount, for leading the project's management team with tireless energy. They would be the first to admit that we would have got nowhere without our incomparable editor, Paul Crick, whose skills as a professional editor have provided the rock on which the *Tales* have been built. He has been ably assisted by the meticulous proofreading of Amanda Flint.

And what can one say about Chris Ellard's cover design and his and Steve Lancaster's illustrations except 'just fantastic'? They are pointed, apt – and funny. You will love them. Enough said.

And then up stepped businessman Colin Keal and his wife Alison, both former PWS students, with generous financial backing and precious business expertise; my sons' company, Handsam Ltd, is also supporting the venture. This financial underpinning has been vital in ensuring that the book saw the light of day.

Other former students also offered their services. Rosie Clarke (née Stafford) and her husband Tony have brought Chris Ellard's cover design to fruition. Kieran Kelly has provided invaluable guidance on sales and marketing.

Many of my friends have contributed ideas, reminiscences and texts and illustrations too. To mention them all by name would require the removal of at least one Tale, but they know who they are and how dearly I hold them.

All of them provided their services free of charge. Thank you, ladies and gentlemen.

We are all grateful to our printers, PrintonDemand. They have played a pivotal role in publishing the book and providing support services which will ensure that the book is available worldwide.

I want to acknowledge my personal debt to the late John Sutton, former General Secretary of the Secondary Heads Association (now the Association of School and College Leaders). His wit and wisdom that I had the privilege to share over many years when I was the Honorary Legal Secretary and then President of the Association inform and enlighten many of the Tales.

Finally, the acknowledgements would not be complete without thanks to all the staff, pupils and parents, who make up a school. If you were not so deliciously funny there would be no book.